CYPRUS -ON- THAMES

BY THE SAME AUTHOR

Hollow Victory (2014)
Field of Dust (2017)

CYPRUS -ON- THAMES

BASED ON A TRUE STORY

Angela Jean Young

ANGELA JEAN YOUNG

The Book Guild Ltd

First published in Great Britain in 2021 by
The Book Guild Ltd
9 Priory Business Park
Wistow Road, Kibworth
Leicestershire, LE8 0RX
Freephone: 0800 999 2982
www.bookguild.co.uk
Email: info@bookguild.co.uk
Twitter: @bookguild

Typeset in 11pt Minion Pro

Printed and bound in the UK by TJ Books LTD, Padstow, Cornwall

ISBN 978 1913913 656

British Library Cataloguing in Publication Data.
A catalogue record for this book is available from the British Library.

To my loving grandparents Ernie and Ada Pridmore

CYPRUS-ON-THAMES

The front of Cyprus is Cyprus Place, by the edge of the Albert Dock, which bristles with scores of cranes, travelling and stationary, dilapidated sheds, and sheaves of chimneys tipped with flowers of smoke. Beyond the dock you may see from your upper window the scarred slopes of Woolwich and the heights of Shooter's Hill. Alongside the dock runs the narrow railway-track, whose station names are so evocative – Gallions, Manor Way, Central, Tidal Basin, Custom House. These names add bitterness to the general atmosphere. 'Cyprus' itself is an ironical gibe. Only one spot here is aptly named – a little street near some allotments, named Savage Gardens.

Cyprus Place is the supply depot of this curious colony, peopled by workers from the docks and the great gas-works. Here are fly-blown eating houses, fly-blown general stores, a newspaper shop, a sweetstuff shop, a few second-hand dealers, and the Ferndale Hotel, the only pub in Cyprus.

Thomas Burke
The London Spy: A Book of Town Travels, 1922
© George H. Doran Company

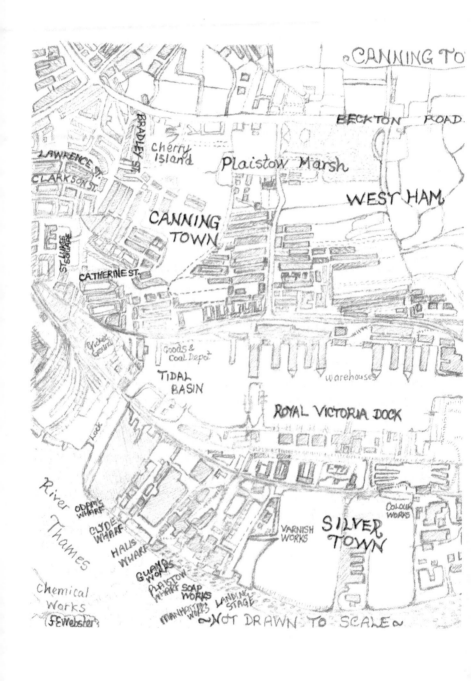

CANNING TO

BECKTON ROAD

BRADLEY ST.

Cherry Island

Plaistow Marsh

WEST HAM

LAWRENCE ST.

CLARKSON ST.

CANNING TOWN

ST LUKE SQUARE

CATHERINE ST.

Pickets Ground

Goods & Coal Depot

TIDAL BASIN

warehouses

ROYAL VICTORIA DOCK

Lock

River Thames

ODAM'S WHARF

CLYDE WHARF

HALLS WHARF

GUANO WORKS

PLAISTOW WHARF

SOAP WORKS

MANHATTAN WORKS

LANDING STAGE

VARNISH WORKS

SILVER TOWN

COLOUR WORKS

Chemical Works

(F.E.Webster)

~NOT DRAWN TO SCALE~

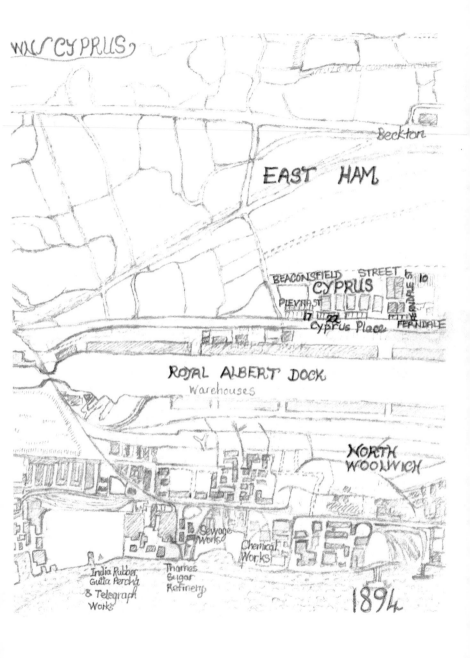

WILKES/PRIDMORE FAMILIES

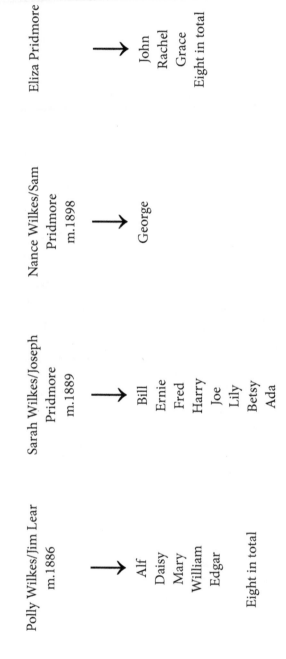

Polly Wilkes/Jim Lear
m.1886

→

Alf
Daisy
Mary
William
Edgar

Eight in total

Sarah Wilkes/Joseph
Pridmore
m.1889

→

Bill
Ernie
Fred
Harry
Joe
Lily
Betsy
Ada

Nance Wilkes/Sam
Pridmore
m.1898

→

George

Eliza Pridmore

→

John
Rachel
Grace
Eight in total

INTRODUCTION

At the end of the nineteenth century, East and West Ham – now part of the London Borough of Newham – were then in Essex. Unaffected by the 1844 Building Act, which restricted dangerous and noxious industries from operating in the metropolitan area, factory after factory was relocated to the marshland on the Essex side of the River Lea. Combined with the building of the Royal Docks, the area's rapid growth, both in terms of manufacturing and population, earned it the name 'London over the border'.

My grandfather, Ernest Pridmore, was born in 1891, part of the third generation of my family to experience the poverty, squalor and uncertainty of being a casual labourer dependant on the docks. His story begins during WW2 and travels backwards in time through a life filled with challenges. You had to be tough to survive and, more often than not, it was the women who proved the toughest, though they paid a heavy price for it.

I have given personalities to people whose sepia photographs, dug out of old albums, were often all I had to bring them to life, apart from what I had been told about them by my grandparents. The events that influenced and moulded Ernie are real. Around them I have weaved the story of our family in Cyprus-on-Thames. For this reason, it seemed only fitting that this should be the title of my book. I can only hope that Granddad would have enjoyed my version of his story.

TUESDAY, 27TH MAY 1941

'Stick this in me hat, Iris… me hands are shaking,' Ada called out to her daughter, waving a lethal-looking hat pin in the air.

'Better get a move on,' Iris responded, shoving the pin into the straw, narrowly missing her mother's ear. The pendulum on the old clock vibrated as it chimed its confirmation. 'Right, that should stop us chasing your titfa down the Mall,' she laughed. 'Are we done then? Can't be late for the King.'

Ernie and Ada Pridmore and their newly married daughter Iris had been up since dawn preparing for their proudest moment – none of them quite believing that in two hours or so they would be entering the gates of Buckingham Palace. The women seemed pleased with their reflections in the hallstand mirror. Begging and borrowing clothing coupons had done the trick.

'Very presentable,' Ada chirped, her knees quivering slightly. 'Do you think we've got time for a final cuppa?' Tea had acquired magical qualities since the war started, everyone turning to it in their hour of need.

'No, we 'aven't!' snapped Ernie, pushing them gently out of the way so he could see if his Port of London Authority cap was on straight. 'We can 'ave one in Lyons Corner 'ouse on the Strand if it's still standing. Come on, we've only got twenty minutes before the train comes.'

Miss Smith's curtains twitched as her neighbours shut their gate.

'Did you see that?' Ada whispered to her daughter. 'I knew she'd be watching.' Then, just loud enough so her nosey neighbour could hear, she added, 'Not everyday someone in Brandon Street gets the *George Medal* for bravery or sees the King pin it on his uniform.' Smugly, she lingered a few seconds to push the leather down between the fingers of her gloves.

There had been a bit of a to-do over who should get to go to the Palace when only two guest tickets initially arrived. Ernie had been cajoled into writing to request two more, which he really didn't think he should do and was not at all surprised when the powers that be wrote back saying no. In the end, on the assumption that Iris's older brother and her husband were more than likely to be at work on the day, it was decided that they were going to have to hear all about it later.

'Blimey, talking about curtains,' Iris said suddenly, 'I didn't pull the blackouts down in the kitchen. We might be back late. Got the key, Dad? You both carry on, I'll catch you up.'

'Better safe than sorry,' Ernie replied, throwing the key to his daughter. 'They're still doling out 'eavy fines for blackout offenders.'

It had been two weeks since the sirens last sounded. Two weeks of everyone holding their breath, waiting for Hitler's planes to cross 'Hellfire Corner' on the Kent coast. It might seem like the Blitz was over, but no one was taking any chances.

The family lived in the centre of Gravesend, a Thames riverside town, twenty-five or so miles east from London. Since the Battle of Britain started in early August, they had become used to seeing Spitfires from RAF Gravesend regularly patrolling the sky. Ernie had erected an Anderson shelter at the bottom of their garden which Ada was reluctant to use at first, but the thunderous noise of enemy bombers seeking out the convoys in the estuary and targeting our inland aerodromes made her nervous. Besides, someone in Arthur Street had been prosecuted for not covering their shelter with the correct amount of earth, let alone not sleeping in it.

Soon Ernie noticed that the waves of bombers were being shadowed by increasing numbers of German fighters which weaved in and out the formations protecting them against attack from our boys. You couldn't help but admire the skill of these young pilots until, later on in the month, a dogfight directly over Gravesend brought him face to face with the harsh reality of war in the air. Hearing the rattle of machine-gun fire, he and son Ernie – home on leave from the Merchant Navy – went outside to see what was going on. They watched in horror as a stricken Spitfire left a burning trail as it cartwheeled down. Their relief at seeing the pilot's parachute open was short-lived as, seconds later, a yellow-nosed Messerschmitt opened fire on him.

Several bombs were dropped on Gravesend that night, damaging the railway line, a school and numerous houses. This, as it turned out, was just a taste of what was to come. On 7th September 1940, the Luftwaffe embarked on a new phase of the battle – the bombing of London – designed to weaken morale as a preliminary to invasion. That night, for the first time since the Great Fire of September 1666, Londoners saw the sky red with flames reflecting off billowing clouds of acrid smoke.

Day and night raids continued relentlessly. On the 15th of the same month, Ada came out of the shelter at daylight only to return an hour or so later, gripping a fresh flask of tea, as the sirens started wailing again. When the all-clear didn't sound she stopped worrying about the Sunday dinner getting cooked and resigned herself to a long wait. Over the next twenty-four hours, five hundred German aircraft fought a running battle with our fighters from Hammersmith to Dungeness and from Bow to the coast of France.

Delayed on the way home from work the next day, Ernie told Ada how a Dornier had crashed just outside Victoria Station causing chaos on the trains. Its crew had managed to bail out, landing by parachute on the Kennington Oval. Unfortunately, as the Dornier blew up beneath him, the Hurricane pilot who shot it down had himself been forced to jump when his aircraft went into an uncontrollable spin. Thankfully, he too had parachuted to safety, in Chelsea.

The London Blitz continued relentlessly until the first week of November, when bad weather curtailed the Luftwaffe's operations.

By this time, more than eighteen thousand tons of high explosives had been dropped, killing 28,556 Londoners and leaving twenty-five thousand in need of hospital care. Six months later, after many other cities and ports had been left severely damaged, the last relentless bombing raid on London took place on 10th May 1941. Another thousand people were killed and a third of London's streets were left impassable. All but one railway line into the capital remained blocked for several weeks.

Closer to home, Tilbury docks and factories along the riverbanks caught the worst of the raids. Incendiaries extensively damaged the Imperial Paper Mill – its pulp stack burning fiercely for several days – and with the water mains damaged, the fire brigade had to pump water directly from the river. Gravesend Promenade was hit regularly by high explosives, one sinking the training ship *Cornwall* moored on the river. A Hurricane crashed on the golf links and a Spitfire on Barton's Wharf – the aircraft buried so deep that recovery of the pilot proved impossible.

Throughout the bombing Ada shared her shelter with a friend from further up Brandon Street. She had chosen not to register her children for evacuation, despite the advice. The day before war started five pleasure steamers took more than three thousand school children from Gravesend's pier to the east coast. Ada had watched wet-eyed as the little ones filed along the street with their gas masks strung over their shoulders and name labels pinned to their coats. She went to Dartford station with Ernie's brother Joe when it was his son's turn to go. Reggie was just seven, and waving him off on his journey to North Wales broke her heart. In all, a million children were sent away from cities to the countryside. One night a bomb demolished a row of houses in nearby Pelham Road, shaking the walls of the shelter so violently that dirt fell down from the joints. After scrabbling to dig out the baby in the dark, Ada could see the sense in the evacuations.

As for Ernie, Port of London tugmaster for twenty years, he knew only too well what Hitler's 'Blitzkrieg' had unleashed. His experiences, right from that first terrible Saturday night, would stay with him for the rest of his life.

It was four forty-five when he'd looked at his watch as the sirens started wailing. From then on it all happened so fast. Someone shouted that the Ford motor works at Dagenham had been hit and within minutes, the giant gasometers at Beckton were blazing. But Ernie knew it was the docks, where he was stationed, that the bombers were aiming for. Huge warehouses and factories on both sides of the Thames were soon ablaze. Two hundred acres of timber stacks, recently arrived from North America, burned out of control at the Surrey Commercial. At the Rum Quay in West India Dock, incendiary bombs fell in clusters, turning it into a raging inferno four storeys high and a quarter of a mile long. A flaming river of spirits and sugar cascaded down the gutters into the water. North Woolwich Road was a bubbling sea of molten pitch and rats were seen swarming out of Knights soap factory in Silvertown. Fire burned through the ropes of barges tethered along the quayside and the burning boats drifted downstream, only to return several hours later on the incoming tide, still alight.

When the all-clear sounded at six thirty, East Enders emerged from their homes and shelters to witness scenes of utter devastation. Fires were raging, houses had been ripped apart by the explosions, and debris and broken glass were everywhere. It was all hands to the pumps – drawn by vans, taxi cabs and anything else that could be pressed into service. Thousands of firemen converged on the blazing dockland, only to be beaten back by the intensity of the conflagration and stunned by its sheer scale.

Two hours later, the sirens went off again. The planes were returning, the huge fires illuminating their target. This time the raid would continue until dawn. Numbed with shock, the nerve and spirit of those affected was tested to the limit that first weekend. Many panicked, not knowing what to do or where to go. Some families loaded their belongings onto prams, carts and wheelbarrows, and headed into Epping Forest, where they slept under the stars.

There were no adequate plans for protecting the people whose lives were being dramatically altered by the bombing. Underground officials had been ordered to lock station entrances to stop them being used as shelters. Angry residents became incensed about the situation and a crowd staged a sit-in at the Savoy Hotel. Fearing an uprising, the Government relented and removed the padlocks. Soon people were sleeping on the platforms, passageways and even escalators overnight. With the days steadily shortening and the sirens wailing ever earlier, streams of women and children making their way to the stations with their bedding became a familiar sight. They waited in orderly queues until four o'clock when they were allowed in and then jostled with passengers until the last train had departed.

Returning to their homes by daylight was an ordeal. Tens of thousands of homes were destroyed or rendered uninhabitable. Streets, littered with rubble, were without gas or electricity, yet somehow, people coped with the situation. They got used to it and, as time went on, came to regard survival as a form of victory.

For Ernie Pridmore, the end of the Blitz – if, in fact, it was – had come not a day too soon. Remarkably fit and strong for a man who was almost fifty, he had been on call throughout the bombing and was shattered. His tug, the *Sirdar*, looked it too. The 168-ton, twin-screw steam tug had been built in 1899 and had already been sunk once. In fact, Ernie had become her first captain when she returned to service after a collision with the SS *Old North State* off Tilbury in 1922, and he had no intention of letting her return to the bottom of the Thames while he was in charge. Stationed at King George V dock, when war broke out the tug was commissioned as one of the PLA's River Fire Patrol vessels. It was the same for everyone working in the docks. Whatever your job, you just had to pull together and do what was required to limit the damage. Policemen moved ammunition from burning warehouses, dockers extinguished incendiary bombs on rooftops, and dockmasters deployed their tugs to save ships and other craft in danger. As the weeks turned into months, Ernie had wondered if there would ever be a *normal* day again.

The train arrived at Gravesend on time, but with so much damage to the tracks its onward journey was slow. Crawling past Lewisham,

Ada could see Bolsoms furniture shop and Chiesmans department store, where she went for her winter coats, had both been badly damaged. 'Woolwich Arsenal's copped it worst,' Ernie said, shutting the window as a pungent smell enveloped them. The two-acre explosive works had been completely demolished, costing the lives of forty-nine men. Bombs had reduced the dockyard to a mass of twisted iron girders. The continuing destruction at Greenwich, Deptford and New Cross silenced the carriage.

'Right, here we are,' Ada announced as the train finally pulled into Charing Cross. 'No time for a cup of tea now. Our tickets say *entry no later than ten fifteen.*'

There were a lot of people outside the gates of Buckingham Palace, but luckily a police officer spotted Ernie brandishing his letter from the Chancery and so ushered the family to a side opening in the huge royal gates. Taking her husband's arm, Ada relished every step as they made their way across the gravel to join a large group of servicemen and others in uniform.

'Can't see much damage,' Iris said, pointing at the front of the Palace. 'I heard it's had nine direct hits. One blew the windows out when the King and Queen were having tea. Miracle they weren't killed. "Now I can look the East End in the face," the Queen said. Oh my, looks like we're going in, Mum. Can't believe it, can you?'

Once inside, the Palace guards, dressed in wartime khaki, ushered everyone into the Grand Hall. A platform had been erected at the front of the ornate room with a slope leading up to it and another coming away. After being instructed on protocol, the fifty or so medal recipients were lined up to the side while Ada and Iris took their seats in the audience. As King George VI, dressed in full naval uniform, made his way onto the platform the room hushed and Iris squeezed her mother's hand.

Nerves started to get the better of Ernie while he waited for his name to be called. As the newly instated George Medal was pinned to his jacket, his whole life flashed before his eyes. He didn't feel like a hero. To him, it was just part of the job. Somehow he and his crew had survived everything the Luftwaffe had thrown at them on those first terrible nights of the Blitz. It had been a scene from hell and they were the lucky ones. Eleven of his colleagues had died when a parachute mine destroyed two other PLA tugs.

As the citation was read out, Ernie stepped forward, bowing before the Monarch.

'Ernest Pridmore, Master of Tug, Port of London Authority, led the first crew of his tug in extinguishing fires caused by incendiary bombs and assisted in preventing serious fires at wharves. He helped to remove laden barges and craft in the docks which were in danger of fire. Throughout the period of heavy raids on the docks Pridmore has shown conspicuous ability, initiative and remarkable devotion to duty in circumstances of extreme danger.'

If only Bill was here, he thought. He'd have been proud to see his little brother being honoured by the King – and even prouder for holding the family together after everything that had happened to them. No one pinned a medal on you for that.

What humble beginnings we all had…

Ernest J. Pridmore GM and Ada. Buckingham Palace.

MONDAY, 22ND FEBRUARY 1897

'Can't you keep hold of them brothers of yours, Bill? They're getting under my feet.' Henry Cook Pridmore was a kindly man and, when he wasn't busy, loved nothing more than rounding up his numerous grandchildren and filling their ears with tales of his upbringing in the Cambridgeshire fenlands. The youngsters, never having been outside of Canning Town, found the stories of marsh sprites and ghostly happenings on the watery wastes exciting and terrifying in equal measures.

However, he found the five boys of his second son, Joseph, a handful. The oldest at seven, and a baby of only three months, were always out wandering the streets, or rifling around his marine stores in St Luke's Square on a cold day like today. With no pram, Bill had to carry little Joe everywhere, so he grabbed at Harry with his free hand, but there was no hope of keeping Ernie and Fred under control.

On days when their Aunt Polly took care of the three youngest, Bill would help Ernie, climb the horse chestnut tree in the churchyard and chuck conkers at the drinkers staggering out of the Charrington Arms into the Square. Other days, when lumbered with all his siblings, Bill had no choice but to bundle everyone inside the marine stores hoping that his grandfather would bring out the biscuit jar. These were the days Ernie loved the best. Enticed by a window full of old medicine, ginger beer, blacking and ink bottles that twinkled when the sun shone, a Peek

9

Frean wafer wasn't half as interesting as the treasures waiting to be discovered within this Aladdin's cave. Rusty anchors, medals, bullets, old flags, sails and torn bunting were just some of the things to be found amongst the buckets of old iron, rags and rope.

In fact, Henry's store bulged at the seams with old bits of ships' furniture and all manner of flotsam and jetsam. Since his wife had died four years ago and his young daughter Eliza was now skivvying over in Leyton, he'd let it get in a mess. Not that trade had suffered. Business was booming with customers eagerly buying under-the-counter stock regularly provided by dockworkers.

He knew he ought to be more careful. By law, marine dealers were required to record, in great detail, all items being offered to them for sale. Name, address and occupation, and even the time and date of the transaction were asked for. It was the bane of Henry's life, but those not complying would be liable for a twenty-pound fine, topped up with another penalty for any stock bought from anyone under sixteen. This stemmed from the old days of paying mudlarks a penny a pound for their finds, but as these children were considered common thieves, local police all too often found dealers guilty of receiving stolen goods. Present-day mudlarks collected coal dropped during unloading. Henry had built up a lucrative trade selling it on to neighbours – especially if it was Derby Brights. No one asked questions, besides the fathers of these muddy boys were well known. Spending too much time in public houses meant they kept their families in destitution.

Not that every man wasted money on beer. St Luke's was in the poorest ward of West Ham known as Tidal Basin. Bounded on the west by the River Lea, it was separated from Silvertown by the Victoria Dock. The majority of its inhabitants were casual labourers struggling to make a living at the dock and no one had a penny to spare.

'It's time you lot went home,' Henry growled, finally having had enough of his grandchildren rampaging around the place.

'No one in, rent man's due.' Bill shrugged, not wanting to leave and rubbing his bare feet which had only just thawed out from the biting frost. His chilblains were red and throbbing. 'And the range 'as gone out.'

Joseph and Sarah Pridmore and their growing family rarely stayed in one set of lodgings long, moving on when they could no longer dodge the rent man.

'Your mother'll be back by now,' insisted Henry, though with little conviction. 'Besides, Joe needs changing.'

Bill dragged out their departure for as long as he could before setting off for Catherine Street, knowing it was likely to be a long wait before Sarah returned from the Flying Scud. They just had to hope there'd been enough money left in her purse for a loaf of bread from Staal's bakers and a few penny bloaters from Rathbone market.

Henry surveyed the bedraggled bunch in their rags and tatters, dawdling down the street. He wondered if they would indeed get something to eat, knowing the state their mother was likely to be in. He'd fed them many times and watched as they scoffed down anything on offer, but they were still very thin and undernourished. Sarah's sisters, Polly and Nance Wilkes, were a godsend when it came to the boys. They were sensible girls and had helped out on numerous occasions when Sarah and her husband Joseph were drunk or in trouble.

How different their young lives were to his own childhood, Henry thought as he picked up bits of broken armour and a cannonball you wouldn't want to stub your toe on. He'd grown up healthily in the Fens, with a mother who'd cared for him. Mary never talked about Henry's father, but his name, Benjamin Cook, was clearly written on his baptism record. Seeing as it said he was a farmer, Henry often wondered if he'd been much older than his mother and maybe married.

Eking out a living in the maze of tiny alleys and passages that made up the Old Horse Fair in the centre of Wisbech, Mary just got on with her life, sewing whale bone into stays and corsets all hours of the day and night until her fingers bled. Henry knew

11

she was doing it all for him and he felt guilty that he had plans other than working in the fields. Like so many, he believed his prospects would be much better in the burgeoning East End of London and had been itching to go. When Mary surprisingly married a local widower and was no longer reliant on her son's earnings, he got his chance to go.

Henry's first London lodging was in a wretched part of Wapping called 'The Ruins', where the coal workers lived and where their wives cured fish in their backyards. Down a narrow, airless alley with a fetid puddle that never dried up, he finally found an affordable private doss-house. Inhabited solely by young working men, they cooked, ate and smoked in silence due to their sheer exhaustion. Thankfully the beds in the cellar had clean linen but – although not being particularly tall – Henry's head touched the ceiling which was as wet as the floor.

'How you liking this poor man's hotel?' asked a lad sitting opposite him at a rough wooden kitchen table. 'Trust me, this is luxury compared to most,' he assured him after seeing the grimace on Henry's face. 'You won't find nothing cheaper round here. There's so many of us come for work, landlords can charge what they like.' The boy dipped his bread in a handful of salt poured out on the dirty table and washed it down with a mug of weak tea. 'You looking for a job, then? I can get you started as a whipper, if you're interested.'

Coal whipping was the new way of moving coal out of the holds of colliers and onto barges before being transferred to the wharves. In the past labourers had shovelled it into baskets and then heaved it up, stage by stage, onto the deck, two men on each stage. Now it was being whipped up by means of a large basket and tackle in a single jerk, making delivery from the hold much quicker.

So, in the summer of 1861, when Henry was just sixteen, he found himself deep in the hold of a collier, covered in grime and choked by coal dust. Filling baskets was hard, relentless work. Quenching a raging thirst with a couple of pints of half an' half at the end of a long shift seemed like a bonus at first, until he found out he was expected to start his day in the public house paying for the same at five a.m., take another with him to work and then buy more drink until he received his wages, often not till bedtime. As the publican kept score and employed a foreman who selected the labour, your life – and wages – were in their hands. And since Henry's landlord was also the publican's foreman, he knew he'd be out of a job, and lodgings, if he complained.

'You should be grateful to me for making you a constant,' the landlord told him. 'Don't want to get a cross against your name. You'll get no work as a straggler. Stragglers never get a look in.'

Henry knew very well what that meant. Constants made up the first gang to be sent out from the ale house when a job came in. Stragglers only got work if all constants were already out and, even then, they'd have to tip the foreman a drop of gin first.

Everyone knew that the business – just like the beer they drank – was less than wholesome. Collier captains paid publicans to put together gangs to whip the cargo and constants went out ship after ship, such was the demand for them. The more they earned, the more the publican earned too – both from the captains and in beer money. Unsurprisingly, the coal whippers had become a drunken and degraded class. After a week of misery, breathing nothing but the impure air from a ship's hold, a man had next to nothing to take home, so their families starved. Even after the Government stepped in and created offices where the men assembled to be picked directly by the collier captains, it wasn't long before the trade was, once again, somehow in the hands of the publicans.

Within a year or so, Henry could take no more and chanced his luck by heading further east to West Ham and the area below the newly built Victoria Dock. Being in Essex and outside London's stricter planning regulations, it had attracted S.W. Silver's rubber works that moved across from Greenwich and gave the area its name, Silvertown. Now there were a variety of chemical works crammed into the space between the dock and the river. Each factory had its own distinctive noise and smell which permeated the streets.

With half of the three million tons of coal transported to central London being unloaded at West Ham, Henry's hunch of more 'coalie' work was right. There was a huge depot in the dock and a public house every few yards along the Victoria Dock Road, where the gangs of coal backers waited to be picked by the foremen. Wearing their distinctive fantail hat, tarred smock frock and half jacket, Henry got regular work with less strings attached, but he had no allusions about it being easier. By bringing the ships alongside the wharf, the merchant saved the expense of whipping. Instead, Henry was now expected to carry two hundredweight sacks of coal up from the ship's hold, sometimes twenty feet down, across several barges via a plank to the waiting waggons. In a twelve-hour shift he and his gang might have to do this ninety times.

'Even the strongest men don't last long in this business,' one of his mates told him with a wry smile. 'And you'll get no sympathy from the bosses if your back's broken.'

Having secured basic lodgings in a row of grey brick back-to-backs just off the North Woolwich Road, it wasn't long before Henry met the Vicarage's scullery maid, Bess Bowden. With lovely walks in the Royal Pavilion's rose-filled gardens, they started courting and it was here that he proposed. The couple married at St Mark's Church on a rainy day in June 1866 and celebrated their union at the Barge House, close to home. Despite its disorderly reputation, they were made very welcome and got a grand view of the newly built promenade.

Bess had also come from the countryside, from Buckinghamshire, and it seemed they'd only been married five minutes when Henry found himself not only supporting his now-pregnant wife but her mother as well. Mrs Bowden had written declaring that she could no longer work in the Amersham fields and was now dependent on outdoor relief of one shilling and two loaves of bread a week from the Overseers of the Poor. Sending his mother-in-law regular monies meant sacrificing their own meagre comforts. Soon, with two children born in quick succession, Henry declared that they could no longer afford to stay in their current lodgings, which, though small and overcrowded, at least were dry. Instead they were forced to find somewhere cheaper, in the oldest and poorest part of Canning Town, close to Bow Creek.

In the early 1850s, this part of West Ham was sparsely populated and divided into Hallsville in the south and Canning Town in the north. With just eighty or so houses, Hallsville accommodated the Thames Ironworks shipbuilding workers, while Canning Town comprised of sixty dwellings in Stephenson and Wharf Street. The navvies building the Royal Victoria Dock lived here, many of them Irish. The lack of planning regulations attracted small landlords who, out to make easy money, built cheap dwellings without roads, pavements, proper drains or gas supply. Two or three yards of clay pipe drained each house into open cesspools, spreading sewage and disease. Sitting on marshland, seven feet below high tide level and with their backs to the ditches, the houses were plagued by damp and often flooded – every block, now and then, becoming an island. A fetid mist rose so high off the ground that people approached like ghosts, only able to be seen from the waist up.

'It's much better since they drained the marsh to build the dock,' Elizabeth Drew, from 2 Stephenson Street, told the Pridmores as they moved in next door. Bess found her strong Irish accent difficult to understand at first. 'Our priest lost his boots in the sludge when he visited Hallsville. Didn't find out they were gone for ages, thick balls of mud was stuck solid to his feet, so they were. You'll still need to watch out when winter comes. Usually floods then and the stink is terrible. Fever from the ague sticks around for months too.'

Henry worked hard to make ends meet while living in Stephenson Street. Bess gave birth to three sons and six daughters as they watched the area grow with many more streets created to house the thousands of itinerant workers from all over the country looking for employment. Eventually two out of every three of this new workforce had been born elsewhere, the colour quickly draining from their skin and their nostrils bleeding from gritty soot soon after arrival. Older streets, like Stephenson with its poor sanitation and drainage problems, were now nothing more than slums. Each house contained two or three families, with extra lodgers paying eight pence a week to obtain nothing more than damp floor space. Given that half of the children in the East End died before they reached five, Bess considered it was a blessing that they only lost one.

When the time came for their offspring to attend school, the new Hallsville National School had opened its doors. It was far more spacious than the original rabbit hutch of a building, where the mistress often had to teach under an umbrella when it rained. Despite all the improvements, though, the back window had to remain permanently shut due to the foul odours rising from the stinking ditch below.

By 1891, with only four children still under their roof, they finally moved to a much nicer house from which they could see St Luke's Church with its small churchyard and trees. They started to save a little money and Henry was able to think about his future. Sadly, though, this new-found comfort came too late for his wife. At fifty-two, and seven years older than her husband, she died in her sleep, her body worn out through childbirth and the struggle to exist.

Henry had no choice other than to soldier on at the dock until the abnormally cold winter of 1894–5 left him unemployed. The upper Thames froze over and huge blocks of ice floated down, causing considerable damage to shipping and rendering the estuary impassable. Water traffic came to a complete standstill and with ships frozen at their moorings there was no work for dockers, coal whippers, porters and the like. Deserted cranes turned into pillars of ice, presenting a constant source of danger to those below. By the beginning of February, whilst thousands of better-off people skated happily on the Serpentine, workers toiling out of doors were dying from exposure as the temperature dropped to twenty-seven below zero. So intense was the cold that even birds froze to death on the branches of trees.

Without work, privation and distress in the area was particularly severe. Henry's sons were forced to turn to the Salvation Army for help, paying a penny a meal for themselves and a half-penny for the children. For Henry, now fifty and with a body bent and twisted from lugging sacks of coal, it was finally time to call it a day. Using what little money he'd manage to squirrel away over the years, he opened a small marine dealership in St Luke's Square.

He'd long forgotten the fresh air and wide-open spaces of his fenland youth, but he was content with what he now had. Wheeling and dealing suited him well, and there was much satisfaction to be gained from being his own boss. These days it was his grandchildren he worried about. Thinking about their little chapped hands grabbing the crumbs from the bottom of his biscuit jar, he knew they would probably go hungry again when they reached Catherine Street. There was little he could do about it, given the amount of trouble that his son Joseph and daughter-in-law Sarah Wilkes were in.

THURSDAY, 25TH FEBRUARY 1897

Henry always believed that his son Joseph was fundamentally a good man. Weak, maybe, when it came to drink, but he had worked hard to provide for his children and most of his money problems were the same as everyone else's. Poverty was everywhere. Having had such a good wife himself, it was Sarah's behaviour that Henry found hard to accept.

Women were central in maintaining a semblance of order and decency, and were often the ones that suffered the most through unremitting toil, just as Bess had. Mothers of large families had an almost impossible job to feed and clothe their children, home working throughout the night trying to make ends meet. Not all were resourceful, and some, like Sarah, constantly drowned their sorrows in drink.

Henry could only watch their inevitable descent into the abyss; his hands were tied. There was now his young daughter to worry about. She seemed to be following along the same path.

'So there's no chance of him standing by you then?' Henry pressed Eliza, daring to hope.

'No, Pa. 'E's long gone. Scarpered as soon as he knew.'

Henry shrugged his shoulders and fell silent for what seemed an age. His daughter hung her head, waiting for his verdict and resigned to her fate.

'You're to carry on charring till you can't work no more, and then go in the workhouse. Best place for an unmarried girl when the time comes. We'll keep the infant until I can find someone to take it in. I don't see any other way.'

Eliza Pridmore was pregnant and alone. A pretty girl with fair hair like her mother, she was a lamb to the slaughter, thought Henry as he watched the tears streaming down her unblemished cheeks. Moving in with her older brothers, in East Ham, for much of the previous year had been a mistake and, in hindsight, was a situation he should never have allowed. Sam was a responsible lad but at only eighteen he faced an uphill battle to stop Eliza being influenced by Joseph and his wife. Twenty-two Cyprus Place was a dark and dingy house plagued with rats due to its proximity to the Albert Dock, which no doubt contributed to the length of time the family spent in their local, the Ferndale.

There were plenty in the public bar who'd take advantage of a tipsy girl of just fifteen and landlord James Young had tried to warn Joseph about it on a number of occasions, but his words fell on deaf ears. So, James wasn't surprised when he heard Rosetta Sawkins holding forth at his counter.

'It was bound to 'appen the way that girl's been carrying on,' she sneered, hands on hips. 'Ripe for the picking, and after what them Pridmores done to me last year, it serves 'em right. Me eye's never been the same since. Doctor Vance can't do nothing more with it. Knocked me senseless, they did. Good thing they cleared off back to Canning Town soon after. *You* remember, don't you, James?'

James wasn't likely to forget. It had been he that ran round the streets of Cyprus looking for Constable Green when it all got out of hand, and he that cleared up the mess afterwards.

Coming out onto the street when he first heard the glass smash, James had seen Sarah Pridmore, dishevelled and worse for drink, waving her arms about and pointing angrily at Rosetta, her next-door neighbour. As he got closer, he realised from Sarah's incoherent babble that Rosetta's brood were being accused of breaking her upstairs window. James thought all the children, including Bill and Ernie Pridmore, looked sheepish, and it was obvious none of them had any intention of owning up for fear of a good hiding.

Unfortunately, that's when Joseph Pridmore emerged from John Brown's Dining Rooms, clearly in a similar state to his wife. Seeing him coming Mrs Sawkins promptly stopped squabbling with Sarah and started on at him instead. That was a mistake.

'You tell your wife to 'old 'er tongue and not accuse my children of breaking your filthy windows,' she spat.

Before she knew anything about it, well-oiled Joseph delivered a fierce blow to her shoulder, hurling a stream of profanities at the same time. Reeling backwards, Rosetta grabbed at the pile of stones the children had collected and made as if to throw them. Joseph and Sarah promptly went for her, hitting one after the other until she fell to the ground unconscious. Satisfied with their work, and with Sarah still shrieking at the top of her lungs, they gathered up their boys and went inside, slamming the door behind them.

Seeing blood spilling onto the pavement, James ran for the policeman, yelling at his potman, Horace Goodnow, to go fetch a doctor.

So severe were Mrs Sawkins injuries that at Stratford Petty Sessions on Wednesday, 19th February 1896, the bench found Joseph Nicholls Pridmore, twenty-six and of Cyprus Place, guilty of a brutal and cowardly assault. He was sentenced to a month's hard labour without the option of a fine. Sarah Pridmore, also summoned for assault, was bound over to keep the peace, her claim that 'another child on the way and four boys to look after' having been taken into consideration.

'Gave the 'ole street a bad name, that family,' declared Rosetta Sawkins after relaying the sordid details of the drama once again to a resigned public bar. 'All over the *East 'am Advertiser*, it was. They called Cyprus *a dreadful place*.'

It's certainly untamed, thought James Young as he surveyed his dejected-looking customers and raised his eyebrows in sympathy with them. Men in their grubby work clothes covered in dust and smelling of smoke, had their lives governed by squalling sirens, hooters and shunting engines. Their talk was slow, mostly grunts and nods. The last thing they wanted after they'd signed off work was a noisy woman in the Ferndale. Public houses were a male preserve; women were expected to call at the off-sales counter with their jugs to be filled and drunk at home. Somehow Mrs Sawkins thought herself the exception to the rule and was lucky that the men were too weary to object. Fights between neighbours were two a penny, and besides, everyone knew of Joseph and Sarah's drinking habits.

The Cyprus Estate, facing the edge of the northern side of the Albert Dock, was an acquired taste. Taking its name from the Mediterranean island now flying the Union Jack, it hardly resembled those azure blue seas and cloudless skies. It was a small, ugly development with broken fences, gasometers and the embankments of a main sewer. There was a lack of mains drainage and its side streets dropped into a waste of ash-heap and half-made road. Mountains of scrap iron loomed above the dock wall, with black dust from the coal sidings and pollution from the gas works clogging the air.

East Ham had witnessed little residential growth compared to its neighbour and even though the Gas, Light and Coke Company had chosen to site their business in the district, the majority of its workforce came from West Ham, particularly Canning Town, and a railway line had been constructed to transport labourers. An industrial village was built close to the works and named after the company's chairman, Simon Beck, but as the company expanded, Beckton soon became overcrowded. Eventually in 1881, a small estate of low and cramped houses was developed close to the newly completed dock, and although originally named New Beckton, with its streets named after past battles, everyone just called it Cyprus. Now that new deep water piers had been built out into the Thames to enable direct unloading from the gas works' own fleet of colliers, there was plentiful work for coal backers like Joseph and his younger brother Sam, who crammed into its rabbit-hutch houses and rooms alongside the gas workers.

Henry Pridmore could do no more than trust that Sam would keep an eye on Eliza until her baby was born. The boy had done well handling Sarah and her children when Joseph was in gaol. But his sister was as headstrong as Joseph was tractable. It was hard to see how either of them was going to stay out of trouble for long. Henry was just grateful that his wife was no longer here to witness their antics. She would have been so disappointed.

'Sam'll look after you, Eliza,' Henry had said finally, after a long time deliberating. 'And I reckon you can take in a couple of lodgers. The rent man'll leave you alone, now that I've paid off Joseph's debts.'

WEDNESDAY, 14TH JULY 1897

Eliza looked around the cheerless lying-in ward at the West Ham Workhouse Infirmary, with its high windows that you couldn't see out of, and wondered how long she was going to be allowed to stay. Its ten iron beds with flimsy mattresses were constantly in use and she doubted it would be long.

After proving she had no means, an 'offer of the house' had been condescendingly awarded. Having given birth, surrounded by the smell of carbolic and Lysol to keep childbed fever at bay, she felt secure in its confines. Apart from being incredibly hot in the grey flannelette institution nightgown with sleeves twice as long as her arms, she'd been better cared for than she might have been elsewhere. There was companionship to be found from girls in the same boat too. Nearly all having suffered mishaps as a result of a spree with a casual acquaintance, some not for the first time, they were relieved to be away from the sneers and jeers of the likes of Rosetta Sawkins.

It had only been a few hours since her boy had been safely delivered, but the wardswoman, a pauper herself, already had her eye on Eliza's spot. It seemed many of the girls were going into the main workhouse once they left the infirmary, Eliza knew she was very lucky that her father had agreed to help rather than throwing her out.

Realising it might be for the last time, she picked up her baby from his shoe-box-sized crib and drew the curtain around the bed for a moment's seclusion. He was a sweet little thing, perfectly formed, and as he eagerly latched on to her breast, she decided to call him John. John William – his second name being the only thing he'd ever inherit from his real father. Even if she wouldn't be able to keep him, no family had been found to take him on yet, so he needed a name. 'No one could argue with that, could they?' she whispered to him.

A few hours later, Eliza and her bundle were on their way down two flights of stairs to find the way out. As they reached the bottom, a woman in the airing ground let out an ear-piercing scream which woke John and made him cry.

'I'd keep going, if I was you,' said an old man. 'Them's just imbeciles. Can't help it.' Standing there in his workhouse corduroy suit, shoes untied and his freshly shaved face raw from a previous lice-infested beard, he looked quite wretched. Covering John with her shawl, Eliza rushed past, determined never to enter the West Ham Infirmary again.

'I'll make sure I'm married before I 'ave another child,' she declared to Sam, who was patiently waiting for her outside the main gates. 'Terrible things go on in there.'

They both stared at the huge eleven-acre site on the Leytonstone Road. Everyone feared the workhouse, it was the last option before starvation, and yet demand for places was increasing at an alarming rate in the West Ham parishes. The infirmary was full of incurable patients from other hospitals, or those who'd lost the family breadwinner. Along with the orphan and foundling children were the families of men who had been transported or were in prison, unmarried pregnant girls and the old who were no longer able to earn a living. Not having to die in a workhouse was what working-class people prayed for. Despite that, more than a quarter of the elderly ended up there.

Sam wasn't convinced his sister would be able to avoid another visit considering her gullible nature. Once a girl got a reputation, a marriage proposal might be hard to come by. He didn't want her ending up like well-known Rosie Werner, whose life alternated between prostitution and spells in the labour ward. Eliza certainly needed telling, but he thought it better to keep his mouth shut since she had every right to throw his words back at him. He needed to put his own house in order first.

SUNDAY, 25TH JULY 1897

John William's baptism was a sombre affair. To keep away from prying eyes, Holy Trinity Church, Leytonstone, nearest the baby's birthplace, had been chosen. The handful of people standing around the font looked in no mood for celebration. Henry had finally located a family willing to take on a healthy child and broken the news to his daughter with some apprehension.

Eliza wasted no time in registering her baby's birth and organising his baptism. Determined to ensure that she would go down, on paper at least, as his mother, he would keep the name she had chosen. There was nothing more she could do.

For his part, Henry was uncomfortable searching for new guardians and, at a pinch, could have allowed her to keep John. But she wasn't ready to be a mother and he feared that, sooner or later, Eliza would take it out on the boy. There'd been many a conversation between him and his late wife as to their young daughter's wayward nature. All his other girls had secured good servant's jobs and stuck at them. No, it was for the best and, as luck would have it, the child was going to remain in St Luke's Square, with a good, honest family – the Batemans.

Henry knew Charlie Bateman quite well. They'd often crossed paths in the Charrington Arms. Twenty years in the West Ham Chemical Works, producing oil of vitriol, had left him with nasal passages damaged by sulphuric acid. Having to breath heavily through his mouth meant he spoke loudly –

something Henry was only too aware of as they put the world to rights over a jug of ale. It didn't do to have people overhearing how his business was going, let alone the fate of a baby grandson.

'You sure your Amelia's happy about this?' Henry pressed him after their initial discussion. 'After all, she's only just had your latest boy.'

'And I doubt he'll be the last,' Charlie sighed, 'even though our oldest is thinking about tying the knot himself. No, put your concerns aside, Henry, he's a bonny lad and she couldn't be happier. And *you* don't need to worry either; everyone round here knows she's a one with the bairns. I've lost count how many she's brought into the world – hardly a week goes by without a knock at our door.'

Henry wiped the froth from his moustache, shook Charlie by the hand by way of sealing their deal and thanked God for finding his grandson a decent home.

Truth be known, Eliza had taken the news better than expected. It was almost a relief after waking up each day wondering if this would be her last one as a new mother. Much as she adored her baby, the responsibility was all too much. Now it was definite and she knew her boy was going to be just across the Square, at least she'd be able to watch him grow.

John William Pridmore opened his eyes wide but didn't make a sound as the holy water dropped on his forehead. A few days later, Eliza handed him over to Charles and Amelia Bateman. They told anyone that asked that he was their adopted son, but there was no formal arrangement and they never changed any part of his name.

SUNDAY, 10TH APRIL 1898

'So our pa's brother is marrying our ma's sister,' Ernie whispered to Bill, scratching his head in bewilderment.

'You got it, clever clogs,' Bill sniggered. 'Uncle Sam is marrying Aunt Nance. It's just they 'ad their George first.'

Wearing an assortment of clothes their mother had bought from the pawn shop, the boys were under pain of death not to get dirty before the wedding, so, with few options, they had decided on the Tidal Basin swing bridge. It was a guaranteed good place to while away the time without getting mucky.

'Don't get it,' Ernie said, having been deep in thought for a while. 'Why didn't we get *our* tidy clothes back from the pawn shop?'

'Gawd, Ern, you're full of questions today. Them outfits'll be long gone by now,' Bill replied with a laugh. 'Ma never 'ad enough coppers to get 'em back, so we 'as to 'ave cheaper stuff. Look, 'ere comes *Dawn* the Stackie. There'll be a bridger, so bell will go off in a minute.'

There were always traffic delays when the bridge had to swing to allow ships in or out of the dock and Thames barge *Dawn* was a regular. She brought in stacks of hay from Essex and took a cargo of fertiliser from the Primrose Soap Works in Silvertown on her return. Despite its sweet-smelling name, this factory produced fertiliser and glue as well as the world-famous Knight Castile soap. Some days it made you want to wretch.

Annie Wilkes sat, somewhat impatiently, at the kitchen table while her sister Polly tried to tame her mass of dark, wavy hair.

'That's the best I can do,' she announced finally, standing back to admire her handiwork. 'The flowers will cover up most of the pins.' Pushing the babies' napkins down one end of the drying line above the range, the pair could now see themselves in the mirror. Only their brown eyes gave them away as sisters. Polly had lighter skin and was fair-haired. There was no mistaking their Irish accent, though. All the Wilkes siblings had the lilt, inherited from their mother.

Having been caged up like wild animals in the scullery, the freed children were now running around the room, chanting, 'Nance is getting married, Nance is getting married.' Annie was indeed getting married, but as the little ones in the family found saying 'Aunt Annie' too difficult, the nickname had stuck and now everyone called her Nance. As baby George headed towards his mother, Nance flashed a desperate look at Polly in fear of sticky hands landing on her bridal gown. Her wedding day had been two years in the making and she definitely didn't want anything to spoil it.

In the February of 1896, when the Pridmore and Wilkes families were dealing with Joseph and Sarah's arrest, Nance had given birth to a baby boy in Polly and brother-in-law Jim Lear's back room. Sam Pridmore, the father, vowed to do the right thing by Nance, but, being only eighteen, had next to no money, so it was decided that the Lears would add baby George temporarily to their own brood so that Nance could find some domestic work and the pair could save for lodgings of their own.

Jim was impressed that Sam had stuck to his word and not been led astray by Joseph, or indeed by Eliza. Many's the time he'd seen the boy out of his depth, forced to hand over his wages to Nance, fearing that it would be spent in the Ferndale if his brother or sister got their hands on it.

Polly thanked God every Sunday that Jim had turned out to be a good husband. He'd not let her down once in their twelve-year marriage. Despite having five children of their own and already sharing the house with another family, he didn't complain when Nance moved in at 8 Bradley Street. Nor when the boys of her other sister Sarah would arrive on the doorstep hungry and hoping for a slice of bread and fish paste, or some bacon rinds – as they had this morning. Jim teased Bill, Ernie, Fred and Harry about their watering mouths when the bacon was frying, whilst restraining little Joe from toddling too close to the range.

Unlike the other children, Polly and Jim's eldest son, Alf, found all the activity unsettling. Bill and Ernie had only just got back from the swing bridge when Jim asked them to take him for a quick walk till everyone else was dressed. Changes to ten-year-old Alf's routine made him agitated. Local kids often took the mickey, calling him 'not right in the head'.

'Just don't go near Cherry Island,' Polly shouted after them. Bradley Street had been built when Canning Town spread eastwards. It was next to a small market garden and gypsy camp and called Cherry Island, as it was surrounded by marsh ditches.

'Why isn't Daisy looking after 'im? She's 'is sister and older than us,' Ernie said as they begrudgingly headed off again. Fortunately, the vinegar and salt man turned the corner and a queue of customers started forming by his cart. Watching him repeatedly sawing two penn'orth of salt off a giant conical block sufficiently distracted Alf.

'She can't,' sniffed Bill, kicking the gravel with the old boots he'd been given. 'She's going to be a *bridesmaid* and can't get 'erself all mucked up out 'ere. People want to look posh on a wedding day – that's why we've 'ad to wash behind our ears.' Ernie wasn't really sure what posh meant seeing as he didn't look that much different from usual in his pawn-shop purchases. A hole was already appearing in the knee of his frayed trousers.

Finally, when everyone was ready, the wedding party walked over to St Luke's Church. Polly was relieved to see Sarah and Joseph waiting outside with Henry and Eliza. At least the family was making a bit of an effort, she thought. That makes a change. She was pleased to see that, although her heavily pregnant sister looked pale and drawn, she was sober. There'd been a nagging doubt about that since her boys arrived early and unfed.

Once inside the church Jim gently stroked Alf's arm to keep him quiet while Polly reflected happily about Nance and Sam finally tying the knot and getting their own place to live. It would be good to have the house back to normal because, then, she could tell her husband that she was expecting again. He'd be pleased even if it stretched his wages. At the end of prayers for the bride and groom, Polly said a silent prayer of her own to keep her husband safe at work and able to bring in enough to keep her away from weekly trips to the pawn shop.

Making ends meet was a constant worry. Jim toiled six days a week stoking the retorts at West Ham Gas Works off the Stratford Way. Although he loved telling people that he was 'changing coal at seven pence per hundredweight into gas at three shillings per foot', all that meant to Polly was that the company was making huge profits while *they* could barely make ends meet on his wage. How anyone could be paid so little for working in such hellish conditions was beyond her.

The retorts – bricked chambers capable of carbonising five hundredweight of coal – were filled by means of iron scoops fourteen feet in length with a bowl at the end holding a hundredweight of coal. There were sixty-four retorts to fill in Jim's building alone, with five other buildings in the works, all kept at red heat by immense coke furnaces. Baking the coal released gas which travelled through iron pipes to huge cylinders where it was stored. After six hours, the stokers then opened the ovens, releasing the blazing coke, which poured out like a molten river. When water was thrown onto it, a whirlwind of scorching black smoke turned the stokers' bodies completely black.

The foremen chose only the strongest to be stokers – those able to withstand the dizziness caused by escaping gas. Even though Jim was at the peak of fitness, he worked slowly in the suffocating heat, lacking the energy to even wipe away the sweat streaming down his body. An old shed with mattresses, as black as the coal around them, was all the men had to lie down on when break time came, and they would collapse there for a couple of hours, covered only by their greatcoats.

Polly continually warned Jim to take care, as it was going from intense heat into the freezing cold that caused consumption. There were many that had gone that way. She would wait outside the gates at the end of his shift with cold water to calm his burning throat, wet cloths to clear his eyes of grit and a dry shirt. Other wives would be there too, all struggling to recognise their husbands amongst the mass of blackened bodies pouring out of the gate. When baby Alf arrived, Polly still came, carrying him on her hip, but within a year he would scream blue murder when the men appeared. Finding his wriggling and writhing too much for her, reluctantly, she had to stay at home. It was then that she knew Alf wasn't like other children and couldn't be left with anyone else. She also knew he wasn't ever likely to earn a living.

Unlike Jim, Sam wasn't strong of body and even on this, his wedding day, he could feel his back straining during the service. Joseph could see it too and felt relieved that his brother had made the decision to stop working as a coal backer and to try something new. Nance had let slip that Sam had his eye on a shop that was becoming vacant and, as soon as the wedding celebrations were over, they were going to see if they could get hold of it. Knowing he had a good head on his shoulders, Polly had little doubt that between the two of them they would be successful. It seemed such a nice idea: Sam, Nance and little George starting a new life as proprietors of a confectioners and tobacconists at 17 Cyprus Place.

TUESDAY, 16TH AUGUST 1898

True to form, on the birth of another baby, Joseph and Sarah dodged the rent collector in Catherine Street and moved back into 22 Cyprus Place. The arrival of Lily, their first girl after five boys, was cause for celebration, and seeing as Sam and Nance had just got the keys to their shop, the Ferndale had a busy couple of weeks. Landlord James Young had been somewhat apprehensive, especially when he caught sight of Eliza flouncing down the street. Now a year older, she oozed confidence as she chatted excitedly to the neighbours. He wondered how long it would be before there was trouble.

Not that they were *all* cause for concern. James had a lot of time for Sam and it didn't take long before he took a liking to Nance too. She was lively and amusing and clearly enjoyed a drink but, more importantly, knew when to stop. She was always keeping an eye on her son and his cousins out in the street, unlike her sister Sarah, who often seemed oblivious to new baby Lily's wailing. With their front doors left open, almost every house had a two-foot-high board wedged in its doorway with a toddler peering over the top and a baby in a pram nearby.

Hearing Joseph slurring his words as he ordered a pint put James on his guard. It was a shame because no matter how hard he tried, he just couldn't see anything of the old Joseph in this beer-sodden man now often fumbling in his frayed pockets for change. The past ten years had certainly taken their toll.

It had been in March 1889 that the two men had first met. James was looking around for a pub in need of a landlord and had befriended Simeon Cundy, who was running the Railway Tavern, by Silvertown station. Mrs Cundy let out their upstairs function room where workers met to air their grievances and over time the pub was just called 'Cundys'. Joseph Nicholls Pridmore was usually up at the front and, despite being young, proved to be a principled and determined speaker.

When a number of men were laid off at the Gas Light and Coke Company, those remaining were expected to work harder and for longer hours. At a protest meeting at Canning Town Hall, worker Will Thorne declared that they should create a union. Joseph was one of the eight hundred who tentatively joined the National Union of Gas Workers and General Labourers formed that evening.

'If you will stand firm and don't waver,' Will argued, 'within six months we'll win. We'll work a six-day week and cut down our twelve-hour day to eight.'

Thorne successfully got the GLCC to meet his demands without the need for a strike and became a local hero. It was while the union were busy signing up over twenty thousand new members that the Ferndale became vacant. James took the pub on and was only too happy to let Joseph promote the union's cause whilst his audience quenched their thirst at the counter.

The year 1889 was significant for the Trade Union Movement, but it also brought great hardship. Inspired by the Bryant and May match girls, dockers in the West India dock went on strike in August for an increase in pay to sixpence an hour – known as the 'docker's tanner'. The success of the strike relied on the support of the whole port and soon one hundred and thirty thousand defiant stevedores, lightermen and coal porters brought the port to a standstill. Whilst Joseph wholeheartedly supported the action, he left the firebrand speaking to others. Being out of work when he had just taken on new responsibilities hit him hard.

Barmaid Sarah Wilkes had first caught his eye whilst standing up to a troublemaker demanding drinks on tick. She was feisty and her quick repartee delivered with an Irish lilt made him smile. Her long dark hair and piercing blue eyes were hard to forget, and it didn't take long before he was smitten – and not much longer before Sarah became pregnant. The couple married at St Luke's that April. Joseph moved in with the Wilkes family at 8 Crown Street and, barely three months later, they were blessed with a son – William. Joseph found himself fighting over the daily meal tickets issued by the unions and often went hungry, only managing to get one ticket for Sarah. The striking men held firm and by early September the dock employers agreed to meet the majority of the dockers' demands. Joseph carried his banner high on the last demonstration in Hyde Park, after pledging to Sarah that it would be his last strike. A regular wage packet would be needed if they were to find a place of their own to bring up their family. There was a lot riding on the young man's shoulders, especially when those deemed to have played a leading part in the action became marked men and needed to be 'disciplined' for what they had done. Some weeks Joseph only got three days' work.

James Young didn't see much of the Pridmores for a few years. Their second son, Ernest, was born in Catherine Street, Canning Town, and Fred in North Woolwich. They returned to Plevna Street in Cyprus for the birth of Harry, and by the time young Joe came along in October 1896 they had gone full circle and were back living at 22 Cyprus Place. By now, they were both drinking heavily and seeing more and more of their earnings disappearing into James's till. Forgetting to register Joe's birth until after the legal six-week limit, Sarah falsified the date. In her haste she omitted to put in their surname. That meant that Joseph's middle name of Nicholls appeared to be his son's surname. Oblivious to the problems this would cause her son as an adult, she chucked the document in a drawer along with all the others.

Year on year, James watched Joseph's personality change. It seemed as if nothing much mattered to him except getting into arguments and fights. After the fracas over the broken window, James was shocked to hear this former man of character complaining bitterly about the injustice of being arrested when all he had done was to separate two fighting women. Incredulously, he hardly seemed to care when sentenced to a month's incarceration.

It seemed inevitable that worse was still to come.

MONDAY, 27TH NOVEMBER 1899

'Ernie… wake up… there's a monster in the river!'

Bill was shaking his brother violently. Ernie wasn't in the mood for jokes, especially after a night of listening to his parents arguing in the next room. No one took any notice of the time in their house.

'What you on about?' he said finally after several attempts to ignore his brother's demands. Sitting up and rubbing his eyes, Ernie could see that Fred was already up and dressed.

'It's massive, Ern. Biggest thing I've ever seen. It come right up out of the water near Cory's coal jetty… about nine o'clock when I was drowning old Ma Tomkins kittens in the river. Got a tanner for doing that. Anyway, if you want to see the monster, we'll 'ave to be quick. There's two tugs chasing it now and it's gone from Galleons Reach right round to Silvertown's Petroleum Works.'

'A *real* monster…?' six-year-old Fred piped up in trepidation.

'One that will swallow you 'ole, if they 'aven't already done it in,' snarled his older brother, chasing him round the room to shrieks of laughter.

Slinging his clothes on, Ernie remembered the rusty armour he'd found in his grandfather's shop and pictured himself wearing it before going into battle against Bill's monster.

It took them more than an hour to walk to Barge House shore and they arrived just in time to see the monster slap its tail in a last desperate attempt to ward off its hunters and drown them in the filthy Thames water. But it was to no avail: the tugs finally rammed the sixty-six-foot female rorqual whale, driving her ashore whereupon the crowd of braying onlookers attacked her with crowbars and hatchets until the river turned red with blood. Hardly believing their own eyes, Bill, Ernie and Fred found themselves cheering with all the others as the poor creature emitted a spout of water forty to fifty feet high just before she expired.

Within minutes, local fishermen had their knives in the thirty-ton animal, while the crowd closed in to buy a slice. With their hands in empty pockets, Ernie and Fred turned away, but Bill rushed forward, ducking between the adult's legs to get to the front. After a few minutes he was back with a large newspaper-wrapped parcel.

'Spent me tanner on a couple of slices for our dinner,' he said triumphantly, straightening his cap with his free hand.

'Reckon we could come back again for another look tomorrow. Might be a bit smelly, though,' Bill continued, holding his nose. Ernie and Fred nodded in agreement, though neither was really that keen to see a rotting monster.

In the event, the authorities decided Royal Victoria Gardens was the best place for the carcass. The steam tug *Empress* dragged it off the beach and towed it back to the North Woolwich shore where it lay, for several days, as hundreds of people came to have their photographs taken standing on top of it or hacking off bits as souvenirs of the grisly affair.

Hungry after their adventure, the boys headed for St Luke's Square.

'You sure this is a good idea, Bill?' Ernie asked, as they reached Pridmore's Marine Stores. 'That sourpuss Maud never looks 'appy to see us.'

'Well, there ain't much point in going 'ome, is there?' Bill snapped as he banged on the door. 'Besides, if Fred don't get some grub inside 'im soon, 'e's gunna cry.'

After wolfing down several chunks of bread smeared with melted dripping, the boys were revived enough to relive the morning's exploits. Henry Cook Pridmore laughed out loud as he watched and listened to his three young grandsons acting out their parts in 'The Slaying of the Thames Monster'. He secretly smiled too as his new wife, Maud, ran around after the exuberant boys. With her duster poised for action, she frantically polished away greasy finger marks before they could dull the shine on her sparkling countertops. Henry could see it was a losing battle, just as the monster's had been.

No one in Canning Town imagined that Henry would marry again – not at his age. However, his elderly mother had other ideas. It was on one of his trips to Wisbech that Henry realised she was becoming frail and needed help. He started paying local spinster Maud Grimsdale a small salary to cook and clean for her. Mary Pridmore took a liking to her carer and suggested to Henry that, when the time came, he could do worse than take her as his wife. Just eight months later – in April 1899 – the domestic married the marine dealer, ten years her senior. Knowing that she would have to move away from the only place she had ever known, Maud accepted Henry's proposal on condition that the nuptials would take place at St Peter and St Paul's Church in the centre of Wisbech for everyone there to see her finally married.

Life in Canning Town had come as a great shock to Maud and she still hadn't got used to it. The rows and rows of terraced houses around Henry's store felt like they were closing in on her, and the grime and noise got on her nerves. Despite having to pass the Little Tommy open sewer on the way, the one and only saving grace was the recreation ground in Hermit Road. But if she wanted to sit down to admire the trees, the benches were often full of sleeping tramps, their clothes caked in gutter mud. Once she found a whole family fast asleep and leaning against one another inside the bandstand, a raw wind gusting round them.

'It's the law of the powers that be that the homeless shall not sleep at night,' Henry had explained to his distraught wife on her hurried return. 'So they sleep by day instead.'

Not liking what she experienced outside was bad enough, but unfortunately Maud wasn't happy with how things were under her own roof either. Henry's laissez-faire attitude to his business gave cause for alarm and the behaviour of some of his children came as a great disappointment. On top of that, there were far too many grandchildren, and she considered Joseph and Sarah's boys completely wild. Despite this, she couldn't let them go hungry when they appeared on her doorstep but was mightily relieved when Henry got them out of her hair by taking them to see the caged birds in Bethnal Green. Parrots, parakeets, canaries and goldfinches – which had been trapped in the Essex countryside – were all for sale in the Club Row and Sclater Street packed Sunday markets.

He also took them to see his local and much-loved football team. Right from the start, Maud had made it clear she wasn't happy about being left alone for too long, but when she realised football was a way of emptying the shop of mucky youngsters she rather took to the idea.

Henry had been enthusiastically following the progress of the Thames Ironworks team since its formation in 1895 by its boss, Arnold Hills. Due to increasing competition from the Clyde and North East of England shipbuilders, only half of the original six thousand workers at London's last major shipbuilding firm were still gainfully employed. Hills believed a football team would help to maintain morale.

Henry sometimes met for a drink in the Liverpool Arms with young apprentice riveter Charlie Dove. He was one of the first to sign up for the team and would head off for training at the nearby Trinity Church schoolroom once he'd finished his pint. Wanting to know what all the fuss was about, Henry went to watch 'The Hammers' defeat Barking 6-2, when Charlie scored a hat trick. After that he rarely missed a home game and, if he knew the team were going on a practice run along the Turnpike Road, would scoop up his grandsons to come and cheer them on – the boys running along behind six-foot-tall Charlie in sheer delight.

Now they were a bit older, their grandfather occasionally took Bill and Ernie to the newly floodlit games. It was a novelty to have the pitch surrounded by light bulbs attached to poles and for the football to be dipped in whitewash to make it easier to see. Charlie Dove was undoubtedly their hero. They marvelled at his skills and were full of pride when the local paper proclaimed him the *finest right half-back in Essex*.

But football had its problems to contend with. For a start, it was a rough-and-tumble game. In the 1897/98 season, it was getting harder to persuade working men to play for the team for fear of injury. Players were allowed to charge by using their shoulder against an opponent's upper body, which caused injuries, and the men couldn't afford to be off work because of them. On top of this, the cost at the turnstiles at the new Memorial Ground was often prohibitive and supporters like Henry were getting thin on the ground. With match tickets costing fourpence, most preferred to spend a penny less at the local musical hall. Not that entry fees bothered Bill and Ernie. If they weren't going with Henry, they'd join the regular gang of boys and climb over the fences to watch the more exciting games the Hammers were playing as they moved up the ranks.

Thames Ironworks had its problems too at the time. Commissioned to build a warship for the Admiralty to rival those of the German battle fleet, work on the ship had been delayed due to lack of manpower and industrial action. When the HMS *Albion* was finally ready to launch on 21st June 1898, around thirty thousand people headed to the yard to watch the Duchess of York do the honours. Henry and Nance shut their shops for the day, Sarah rounded up her boys, and Polly, after a lot of soul-searching, even allowed an excited Alf to join in too. As they crossed St Luke's Square, Henry saw Amelia Bateman setting off with her brood. Little John Pridmore was walking now and was making a fuss about having to go in the pram. His manner was so reminiscent of Eliza that Henry couldn't resist ruffling his blond curly locks as he passed by.

All the shipyard workers had been given the day off and, with their families in tow, were packed like sardines on the quayside. Henry saw about two hundred people clamber onto a temporary slipway bridge next to the nearly completed vessel. He was tempted to join them but at the last minute changed his mind. With so many children, including Alf, to look after, it was better to avoid the crush.

The crowd waited with bated breath as the Duchess took three goes before the champagne finally smashed over the hull, signalling the release of the *Albion*. Everyone cheered wildly, sirens and horns shrieking as the ship slid down the slipway into the water. It was all too much for Alf, who screamed and tried to make a bolt for it. As Polly and her sisters tried to restrain him, no one in their group saw the huge backwash sweep all the spectators on the flimsy bridge into Bow Creek. The first Henry knew of it was when he saw a workman dive from the quay wall into the murky water and return to the surface with a screaming woman, baby in arms. Realising what had happened, he watched – half in horror, half in relief – as a dozen small boats closed in on the scene and started pulling people out of the water. One boat alone rescued fifty people, some having to be resuscitated by artificial respiration.

Tragically some couldn't be saved, and after witnessing a young mother being pulled out of the river with her two lifeless daughters still clinging to her skirts, Henry shielded his family and quickly ushered them all out of the shipyard. Amazingly, the majority of the crowds filing out alongside them were still unaware of the accident.

Arnold Hills was devastated. He visited all the bereaved families and paid the funeral expenses of the thirty-eight who died in the accident. Sadly, most of them were women whose heavy clothing gave them little chance of survival. They were buried in a communal grave at the East London Cemetery the week after. Henry was amongst the hundreds that gathered along the route of the funeral procession.

It was hoped that the new 1898–9 football season would help take the workers' minds off this terrible event. With attendances averaging only one thousand, the club was running at a loss, so Hills had no choice but to recruit some professional players to attract larger crowds. As a result, the fortunes of the club soon improved, the Hammers winning five of their first eight games. In the New Year's Eve match Charlie Dove was acclaimed for playing in every position for the team when he deputised for the regular goalkeeper who had missed his train.

Ernie could never have imagined that a year later he'd be watching his team amongst a crowd ten times bigger. Now renamed West Ham United, losing 2-0 to arch-rivals Millwall was made all the more painful thanks to Dove's superb tackling skills now playing for the other side.

WEDNESDAY, 20ᵗʰ JUNE 1900

The parade was three miles in length as it wound its way through the East End and took an age to reach Canning Town. Thousands lined the streets waiting to cheer on the patriotic march for South African war widows and orphans. Nance was busy selling miniature flags in her shop and Jim Lear, along with all his neighbours, was out in the street putting up banners and bunting. He'd even pinned a *Stratford Express* picture of the King on the front of his house. No matter how poor people were, supporting the war was a matter of national pride and decorating their houses was a way of showing it.

As the sound of the first marching band reached the ears of the huge crowd the cheering erupted. Daisy and her brother William Lear, along with their cousins Bill and Ernie, broke away from their mothers and found a spot close to the main road. They could hardly believe their eyes as band after band passed by, followed by soldiers in uniform, men on horseback dressed as cowboys and floats with banners saying *Britannia Rules the Waves*, *Our Empire's Defenders* and *Mafeking Fort*.

'Bit different from the dockers' demonstration last week,' Polly said dejectedly as the last group of boys dressed as Baden Powell and Kitchener disappeared into the distance. 'They only 'ad *one* brass band to support them.'

'Still, we cheered 'em on as best we could,' Sarah responded, unable to hide her irritation. Despite his promise to the contrary, her husband had become totally absorbed by the strike, staying out all hours for the cause. Today was the first time she'd been able to go out since her second daughter had been born. 'Joseph's still manning the picket line, but I can't see the strike lasting much longer. Stevedores ain't coming out. Worst of all, union's short of money. We've only 'ad one payment of four bob. I keep telling 'im 'e'll 'ave to go back on the colliers. Got no milk for little Betsy, see?'

She stopped just long enough to take a breath. 'To be 'onest, Poll, I consider meself lucky 'e 'asn't spent more time inside. There's been plenty of dockers that 'ave. I thought 'e'd get arrested when 'e went in the Liverpool Arms with Fred Pearce and saw two blacklegs at the bar. Fred got seven weeks for punching one of 'em on the jaw.'

'It ain't fair,' agreed Polly. 'There's been no mercy for the dockers. Old Mrs Connelly's 'usband got six weeks 'ard labour for getting in a fight. Terrible shock, seeing as 'e's an old man. And when one of them rats from the *Lady Jocelyn* smashed the Tidal Basin Tavern's windows, the blighter didn't get so much as a warning from the judge.'

For months, enlisted men, officers and horses had been filing into the Albert Dock in their thousands, embarking on ships bound for the South African War. An immense feeling of patriotism was shared by all those living close by, and young Ernie would often be gazing in awe at the soldiers' packs and rifles and smart felt hats with their regimental crests. Nance and her son liked standing on the Connaught Bridge watching handkerchiefs and flags being waved between the soldiers and their families, George grasping his mother's hand as the gangways were removed and ropes cast off.

Joseph had been reassigned from coal porterage to loading munitions and helping wounded soldiers off the hospital ships returning from the conflict. But at the beginning of June a problem had arisen. Scruttons Ltd, the newly appointed labour contractor for Victoria and Albert Docks, started hiring dockers from those already inside the gates rather than giving everyone outside the gates a chance of work. Those locked out forced their way inside, went to the ships and called out the men, most of whom stopped work. Scruttons, aided by the dock and metropolitan police force, locked the gates to the striking men.

On 9th June, four days into the strike, news arrived of Pretoria's surrender to the British. Almost immediately, every ship in the Victoria and Albert Docks blasted their horns and began hoisting flags from stem to stern. Tugboats kept up an unceasing round of hooting and barges were decked out in the national colours.

With public sentiment for the war on their side, Scruttons, supported by the strike-breaking Shipping Federation, responded to the walk-out by calling in non-union labour from elsewhere. Blacklegs were promised twelve months' regular employment at thirty shillings a week with accommodation on Federation vessels which could be sent wherever they were needed. The old three-masted sailing ship *Lady Jocelyn*, moored in the docks, housed five hundred alone, and when she was full, makeshift accommodation for several thousand strike-breakers was found in sheds and other boats.

As the Federation brought in more blacklegs, the union attempted to widen the dispute by sending pickets to the other docks. That's when things began to turn nasty. Fights between union men and blacklegs broke out in the pubs, but strikers who got arrested were shown little mercy in the courts. Men like Joseph, who were manning the picket lines, found themselves torn between backing the strike and supporting the war effort. People were saying that men who refused to load troopships were 'blacklegging the soldiers defending the empire', and local papers were full of how troopships were being delayed by the strike. They claimed *the union was undermining patriotism for the Boer War*. Dockers appealing for help to feed their families were seen to be in conflict with those collecting for war widows. On top of all this, the Government let it be known that if coal porters failed to load the transports, it would recruit labourers who would.

Coal porters
photographed by George Davison about 1900

SUNDAY, 7TH OCTOBER 1900

'It's not surprising the fools got caught.' Joseph smirked, taking a long swig of his beer. 'Fancy leading the 'orse down Auberon Street where a copper lives.'

Sam nodded in agreement. 'They 'ad nearly twenty 'undredweight, so I 'eard.'

'Bloody unlucky, that wheel falling off,' Joseph continued, wiping his mouth with the back of his hand. 'Now they'll be for it.'

It was dinnertime and the Ferndale was packed with dockworkers, porters and the like on their day off. Everyone was animated about the previous night's heist from the Albert Dock. Two dockers had made a hole in the perimeter fence and filled their horse-drawn cart with gun-metal bearings and other machinery and very nearly got away with it. Everyday pilfering didn't raise an eyebrow, but news of a daring robbery spread like wildfire amongst the ale houses.

A docker's life was generally bleak; the vast majority were casual labourers who clamoured for hire outside the dock gates. The poor policeman, who stood in the middle of Connaught Road directing traffic, had no chance when it was time for the 'call-on' at the Royals. At seven forty-five every morning, five thousand dockers would surge towards him, blocking the road. The lucky ones to get picked – often bribing foremen with whatever they could afford from their meagre earnings – risked breaking their necks falling into a ship's hold or being crushed during loading. Cargo which was often dangerous to handle, like sulphur and pitch, could blind for days at a time.

With the dock strike coming to nothing, the men had drifted back to work in July. The dock owners celebrated having beaten their employees, as well as the union, and reported with pride to their shareholders that wage costs as a percentage of receipts were the lowest they had ever been. Petty pilfering, on the other hand, had accelerated at an alarming rate.

The great irony of dockland life was that workers handled goods they would otherwise never have come into contact with. Walking on half-inch layers of sugar, ankle-deep in currants, haricot and soya beans, the men passed huge ivory tusks and hides, chunks of coral and buckets of quicksilver, all stored inside the docks enormously high walls. Currants and haricots are good food, but when a bag had burst, the correct thing was to tread them into the floor. Any dockman scraping up a handful of dusty currants to take home for a pudding for the kiddies would find himself accused of theft. However, the temptation was immense, and heading home with a bottle of brandy dangling on string in each trouser leg and pockets full of tobacco and tea was common. Unsurprisingly, many of these procured delights from all corners of the Empire ended up under the counter at Henry Pridmore's Marine Stores. Jordan almonds, oats, wheels of cheese, pineapples, grapes, cooked tongue and condensed milk sat alongside bottles of chlorodyne to cure the resulting upset stomachs. With such miserable rates of pay, many dockers depended to a degree on petty larceny. It wasn't without risk, though. Random searches at the dock gates meant that the Thames Police Court was always busy, and sentences dished out frequently involved weeks of hard labour.

If the men weren't apprehended smuggling out unopened bottles, they were often caught actually drinking on the job. The wine vaults were dark places, lit only by torches and the long corridors were lined with raised rails to make trundling barrels easier. On one occasion – which caused great hilarity in the Ferndale – an entire gang of stevedores had been found 'sucking the monkey'. This entailed going into work with a tube hidden in your clothes for the purpose of sucking wine out of a barrel. These stevedores, loading the hold of the *Winkfield* bound for South Africa, were all inebriated. One man was so drunk that he had to be hoisted from the hold to the dock in a basket. Unfortunately for Richard Cornelius Foster, foreman of the gang, two months' hard labour was the penalty for the misdemeanour.

SUNDAY, 7ᵀᴴ JULY 1901

It was Ernie Pridmore's tenth birthday. Not that he expected the day to be different from any other; he was just glad it didn't look like rain. His gang had decided to play 'knock down ginger' after all of their chores were done and, as it was his birthday, the daring job of rattling the door knockers and diving out of sight was his. Most children spent their days in the street, be it keeping out of the way of mothers doing housework or shift workers sleeping. There were fewer creepy-crawlies outside too – apart from the ones you carried about with you in your hair.

One of their boarders, John Toy, worked all night cleaning printing machines, so he slept during the day in the boys' room. Consequently, Bill and Ernie had to be up early to take their little sisters, Betsy, who still wasn't walking, and baby Ada Mary, to Aunt Polly. Despite being pale and underweight, Ada had lungs big enough to emit deafening screams so there was never any time for breakfast. On return they'd round up Fred, Harry, Joe and Lily. Now three and prone to tantrums, Lily was a nuisance to be dragging around all day. It all seemed a bit odd to Ernie. He'd heard people saying things were going to get better for the working class now that the old Queen had died, but somehow his family seemed worse off.

They were back in the oldest part of Canning Town, in one of the sixteen streets added as the Thames Iron Works expanded. Fifty-four Lawrence Street was a terraced house that had been adapted for letting to two separate families. The Pridmore family lived in the three rooms upstairs, and although a range and sink had been installed, the only copper for hot water was downstairs so the tin bath didn't get much use. To make ends meet, the family below had taken on three additional boarders – the Toys. John was the eldest at seventeen, and then came his sisters – collar ironer Nellie and sewing machinist Norah, who was just fifteen. With no one looking out for them, this tightknit trio worked long and hard to be able to afford what little accommodation they had. The girls' room opened into the wash house, offering little light and air and was always damp, and a makeshift bed had been put up in the kitchen for John. But as the water closet was in the yard and the entrance to the yard was through the kitchen, everyone tramped through it – hence Ernie having to give up his bed during the day to let the poor lad get some sleep. The arrangement suited Joseph and Sarah because, by common agreement, some of the young man's rent now came to them.

The girls spent all their free time and money at the Royal Albert Music Hall at the top of Victoria Dock Road and were always singing and dancing. They taught Lily the words to their favourite song, 'The Boy I Love Is Up in the Gallery' and had Ernie in stitches with their jokes picked up from the stage. He longed to see Vesta Tilley and all the other acts and, sometimes, when his parents were out drinking in the Flying Scud, he'd stand outside Canning Town station watching the huge audience pouring out of the brightly lit venue with its glittering chandeliers.

Despite such distractions, Ernie was sorry they'd left 22 Cyprus Place. He'd been used to moving home in the past, but having been settled for nearly three years, this time leaving was more difficult. He'd made a bit of a name for himself locally by never turning down a job that might pay a wiry lad a few pennies. Scrambling under the workbench for tiny nails and tacks dropped by bootmaker George Pratt at number 14 was a perfect case in point. Luckily Aunt Nance had a ready supply of humbugs and just the ointment required to sooth his knees, which resembled pin cushions.

Knowing Joseph and Sarah of old, everyone in the street kept out of their way, and with Sam and Nance keeping an eye on their drinking, there hadn't been any concerns for a while. With a little more money in the housekeeping, things had improved, and that's what had kept the family's heads just above water. Nance got on well with the other shopkeepers in the street, and out of respect for her, they helped out by parcelling up their curled-up bacon scraps or wilting cabbage leaves at the end of the day for collection by one of Sarah's children. Fishmonger Fred Philby could never resist Ernie's toothless grin and his wife often chucked in a pint of winkles with the broken sprats when she saw his doleful blue eyes looking in the window. Sarah had been earning a shilling or two scrubbing the floors of John Brown's Dining Rooms while son Bill made a few extra bob disposing of unwanted kittens. With rats pouring out of the docks, everyone had a cat, so keeping the feline population down was a necessary evil.

They had just about weathered the storm when second daughter Betsy was born in March 1900, but being told he was going to be a father yet again at the beginning of the New Year seemed to tip Joseph over the edge. He was barely thirty, and being responsible for eight children suddenly didn't sit well on his shoulders. Leaning on Nance's counter while he waited for the free tobacco she regularly doled out to him, he declared that he didn't see why he should *back coal* for the rest of his days to feed so many mouths. He wasn't appreciated. His paltry wage, greedy landlord, and the Early Breakfast House in Beaconsfield Street no longer letting him have his fried bread and bloaters on tick... none of it was fair.

Fair or not, this was just the way things were. A man and woman marry and set up home in one room. Their income does not increase with the years, though their family does, and the man is exceedingly lucky if he can keep his health and his job. More and more babies come, extra rooms are desperately needed, but with so many mouths to feed that becomes impossible. It may come as no surprise that in 1901, West Ham had the largest population of children under fifteen in the whole of the county of London.

Soon, Joseph was back leaning on the Ferndale's counter. Sarah was quick to follow suit and the rows started again. The pub had recently changed hands and manager Arthur Barnett wasn't prepared to put up with any nonsense. Just about every man in Cyprus Place was a coal worker, gas stoker or dock labourer, and they all worked damn hard. Joseph's arrogant manner and cursing finally got him banned. All the goodwill Nance had built up quickly evaporated, shop doors closed and her sister was back to dodging the rent man again. It couldn't carry on. Nance was sure Sarah would lose the baby if she continued like this, which was when older sister Polly stepped in and found the family the rooms in Lawrence Street, not far from her and Jim.

SUNDAY, 29TH SEPTEMBER 1901

Eliza gently rocked her tiny daughter sleeping soundly in her arms. It had been four years since she'd last stood at the font of Holy Trinity Church, Leytonstone, and this time only her father was there to see Rachel Elizabeth baptised with the minimum of fuss.

Most of the family just shrugged their shoulders when they heard Eliza was pregnant again. They were, frankly, surprised it hadn't happened sooner. Henry's new wife Maud, however, had plenty to say about it. Bending her husband's ear relentlessly, she banged on about how Eliza ought not to be relying on her father's money for her keep. At twenty, she should know better than to get herself into trouble again.

Henry had worked hard to find a family willing to take in his newest granddaughter in the two weeks since she'd been born, but to no avail. Girls were considered more of a burden than boys. He'd even asked the Batemans, but Amelia had given birth to a girl of her own after taking in John and, with six of her nine offspring still living at home, couldn't possibly entertain another. There was nothing else for it but to leave Rachel in the hands of the authorities to find suitable foster parents.

There was absolutely no way Eliza could have kept her new baby, not at 37 Clarkson Street. It was a horribly overcrowded two-up two-down terrace with an outside wash house. A fellow and his three sisters lived downstairs while Otto and Beattie

Vick and their two young children were in one room upstairs. Eliza paid them a shilling a week for the other. With a single bed occupying more than half the space, there was no room to swing a cat.

'There's rising damp from the rotten floorboards and no water up here,' Otto warned her. 'Well, not until it rains.' He laughed, pointing to a hole in the ceiling through which Eliza could see daylight. She could also see that the remaining ceiling and surrounding walls were covered with blood marks and splotches – each mark representing a violent death of an insect. Bed bugs and lice were a fact of life no matter how many times Beattie Vick tried to exterminate them, and she lived in fear that her beloved girls would succumb to diarrhoea or, worse still, typhoid, so prevalent in the summer months. 'We've begged the landlord to make repairs,' Beattie sighed, 'but he never comes.'

With hardly any money between them all, a cup of milky cocoa was all Eliza could expect before she set off for work in the mornings. After giving up John, she'd got a job as a factory hand making boiled sweets and butterscotch at Keiller's confectionary and marmalade factory on Tay Wharf, Silvertown. The sickly smell from boiling molasses took some getting used to and it was scalding work for the workers, the majority of whom were women. It was also women who did the barge work at Keiller's. It took eight girls to load a barge with jars of jam and other produce. With so little room in the hold, it was a backbreaking job and one Eliza had dreaded. Not that her turn came round a third time; just as she was getting her head above water, the factory was completely gutted in 1899 when a gas explosion caused a huge fire. The 1,400 staff were laid off whilst it was rebuilt.

Luckily for Eliza, the Beacon Coffee Palace in Stratford's High Street had been leased to an Austrian, Morris Streimer, who was looking for staff. He had manufacturing premises on Ward Road, where he made French Nougat – advertised as *the favourite up-to-date sweetmeat*. Eliza had no idea what nougat was, but she was soon making tons of it and watching it being snapped up from street traders at fourpence a slab.

Henry had been pleased with his daughter's progress but, knowing it wouldn't take much to cause an upset, felt concerned when Joseph and Sarah returned to Canning Town. The houses in Lawrence Street backed onto those in Clarkson Street with the Huntington Arms on the corner. Inevitably, it didn't take long before landlord Thomas Moorley had to deal with the unruly behaviour of his new customers. Eliza often couldn't remember how she got back to her house after closing time. Some nights, she'd take the wrong turning close to the River Lea and find herself wading in filth. Raw sewage washed upstream when the filters couldn't cope, flowing onto the streets, the stench spreading across the whole of West Ham.

Not that vile smells were that unusual. At 48 Rathbone Street, James Evans, a dealer in meat for cats, bought horseflesh in large quantities from the local knacker's yard and supplied an army of hawkers with slithers of meat skewered on bits of wood to sell at a ha'penny a go. One of the hawkers, Edward Kennett, had so many regular customers that he would post a thrupenny bit's worth through letterboxes and get paid weekly. Eliza couldn't help but smile as she passed this Pied Piper most mornings being followed by a clowder of cats. He'd often have a kitten or two hanging from his blue apron strings as he pushed his wooden barrow. They got to talking, Edward started visiting the Huntington and then one thing, sadly for Eliza, led to another.

'London's divided up into *walks*, you see,' he had explained a week or two after she told him she was carrying his child. 'We're born and bred in the cats' meat business. I inherited mine and it's my private property, if you like. It's worth more than twenty quid. Now, I've 'eard of another walk where the current holder is retiring. It'll mean I can better meself, Eliza. It's a good one, worth as much as an 'undred and fifty. I'll send for you as soon as it's all settled and I'll 'ave enough for a nice wedding.'

Six months later, on 13th September 1901, with no man in sight and nowhere else to go, Eliza gave birth to her second child in the Union Workhouse Leytonstone.

MONDAY, 9TH JUNE 1902

It was generally accepted that casual labour was responsible for the worst evils in West Ham. Drunkenness, cruelty, theft and prostitution were all traceable to the operation of the system. Poverty due to irregular work at Victoria Dock and the Silvertown factories had been an unwelcome fact of life in the surrounding streets long before Henry Cook Pridmore came seeking work. There was massive overcrowding in the Tidal Basin, the opening of the Albert Dock in 1880, followed by the dockers' strike a few years later exacerbating the situation as more and more labourers flooded in from the countryside.

Being close to the site of the 'call-on' was vital for the dockworkers, but with casual labour so easy to obtain there was no incentive for employers to offer regular jobs. Hordes of men would head to the pitch on the north side of Victoria Dock at fixed hours of the day in the vain hope of being handed a metal tally ensuring a job. Sometimes, foremen faced with a sea of desperate faces would just hold the tickets out to be snatched, or throw them up in the air, rather than make a selection. Henry witnessed the ensuing fights, sickened at the demoralising effect this had on the men.

He also saw the desolate line to enter the workhouse casual ward start to grow before three every afternoon. They didn't 'let in' till six and although the men knew that only the first twenty or so would be accepted, they remained glued to the spot in the slender hope of getting in by some kind of a miracle. Many of these men had answered the call for extra labour in the docks due to the war in South Africa but were now vagabonds 'on the doss'. The harsh laws made sleeping, or dossing, the hardest problem they had to face, harder than that of food. After a rest up in the 'casual', they were good for another two or three days and nights on the streets.

Maud was desperate to move back to Wisbech, and although her husband was well aware she was much better off than most of the women in his family, he could see that her health was deteriorating and had agreed to think about going. There was no denying that the winter fog mixed with the black smoke emitted from surrounding factory chimneys was debilitating. It formed a dense, oily vapour which lasted days. At one time, after the whole of Beckton had been enveloped in exceptional pollution created by the gas works, damp white particles in the early-morning air became coated in soot, which were pungent to inhale. Nance brought George to stay with his grandfather till it was over and had the devil of a job getting back to the shop after having to abandon her omnibus in the traffic chaos. Henry smiled at Nance fussing over her son and giving Maud a list of his likes and dislikes. As Nance's only child, he was understandably precious. By comparison, Sarah's eight – with a mixture of unhealthy pallor, constant runny nose and barking croup cough – were clearly neglected. Things were going from bad to worse and their welfare was contributing to Henry's reluctance to leave.

Joseph hadn't long joined Bert Brown's coalie gang on the derricks, and his excessive drinking was made all the worse by having to hang around for the leading hand to carry out the call at the nearby Railway Tavern. It was also where they waited to be paid at the end of the job and where Bert bought them all a restorative drink. No permanent men were employed, and the hiring was left entirely to the gangers, who had their own lists of experienced men to summon. The work was very irregular, especially if the weather was bad, and then, if several ships docked at once, the call could last thirty-six hours at a stretch. No man could work under pressure for more than six or seven hours without a rest, so relief gangs were taken on to work alternate shifts. Watching her husband dragging on his clothes every morning, it was obvious that he was no longer at the peak of fitness. Sarah worried that sooner or later he wouldn't be picked.

On top of all this, the number of coalies required at both the Victoria and Albert was falling steadily. The introduction of labour-saving machinery like coal scooper 'Long Mike' only needed one man to look after it and another to trim the barges when they were nearly empty. Some weeks Joseph only earned a paltry ten or eleven shillings, which he blamed for their declining circumstances. Getting five out of him for the rent money was becoming a real struggle for Sarah.

THURSDAY, 2ND APRIL 1903

The noise inside Barking Public Hall was deafening – the crowd baying for blood as Bill and Ernie squeezed through heaving, sweaty bodies to reach the ringside. They'd been loitering outside for some time hoping the doorman's back would be turned long enough for them to dodge past. Most of the audience were chanting for boxer Pedlar Palmer to win, but when a few brave souls started yelling support for his opponent, Fred Delaney from Woolwich, the crowd surged dangerously. Up till now Ernie had only seen pictures of local hero Thomas Palmer on the back of a discarded *Boxing Fights* magazine. He and Bill copied his sparring stance when they sized up against each other in the yard and pestered their father to read the best bits about him over and over again. Ernie could recite one bit word for word – *Quick and agile as a cat and called the Box o' Tricks, he was here, there and everywhere, putting into execution more dodges than any two ordinary men.*

The crowd started stamping their feet as Palmer entered the ring, dancing around frantically and punching the air. Ernie watched wide-eyed as the ex-World Bantamweight Champion skilfully defended himself, dodging the blows through pure speed and ring craft. Shouts of 'knock 'im out!' came from all sides, yet at the end of the bout both men were still standing. Everyone waited with bated breath until the referee declared Pedlar Palmer the winner on points.

'That's 'ow 'e's won most of 'is matches,' declared Ernie as they made it out into the spring fresh air. 'Not called "Bag o' Tricks" for nothing – 'e's blooming marvellous.'

The boys stood outside the Welcome Coffee and Chop House until the delicious smell of unattainable food became unbearable.

'Let's go and 'ang about by the tram stop,' Bill suggested with a wicked look in his eye. 'I'll 'ave a go at geeing up the 'orse and see if someone'll drop a tanner buying a ticket.'

'Reckon I'll be able to box like Pedlar Palmer soon,' Ernie piped up, still lost in thought over the boxing match.

'Pa'll be pleased.' Bill laughed, aware that his brother hadn't been listening to a word he said.

Joseph Pridmore had known Thomas and Matthew Palmer since they were children chasing up and down Forty Acre Lane together. Their father, Robert, worked in the docks and was a bare-knuckle fighter who told everyone he was the champion of Essex. His wife bragged she could take on any woman in the East End too.

The Palmers' boxing shows entertained audiences in fairground booths and music halls, and Thomas, despite being little more than five feet tall, was a master showman and naturally talented boxer. He had a number of fights, including some bare-knuckle ones, before he won the British version of the World Bantamweight Championship in 1895. At only nineteen, he was the youngest boxer ever to win the title, earning him the nickname 'Pedlar' due to his ability to back-peddle out of trouble in the ring.

Joseph and Sarah had joined hundreds of well-wishers clambering to get close to Holy Trinity Church when Pedlar married. Unfortunately, marriage didn't calm him down, and though he successfully defended his title over the next three years, he gained a reputation for living as fast outside the ring as inside. Eventually his devil-may-care lifestyle took its toll and when he went to America in 1899 to fight their top bantamweight 'Terrible' Terry McGovern, he was demolished in the first round. After that, his form began to go downhill. Ernie refused to believe his hero was finished as a fighter, and on hearing Joseph and Pedlar's brother, Matt, talking boxing over the counter of the Palmer family's tobacconist shop in the Barking Road, convinced himself Pedlar was set for a successful comeback.

'You're right, Ern,' Bill acknowledged, rubbing his jaw. 'You're getting to be a good little boxer.' The brothers put their shirts back on, jumped up on the wall separating the neighbour's privy from theirs and sat relishing a sticky toffee apple they'd bought with their finds. 'Reckon you're about ready to join the Forty Thieves.'

Ernie smiled broadly; it had been his dream for ages to join his brother in such a respected gang.

'They don't just let *anyone* in,' Bill clarified. 'Got a reputation to keep and you'll 'ave to be my apprentice for a bit.'

Ernie didn't care; he just wanted in. He and Bill, and even Fred, did a fair bit of lifting whenever their ma told them there was no money for food. There were shops all along Victoria Dock Road – Ubele's sausages at 104 and Maloney's sprats at 101 being the easiest to grab. With eight mouths to feed, Sarah was relieved when the boys emptied their pockets onto the table. Turning a blind eye to where the food came from wasn't something you thought too much about.

Bill had known for a while that something was very wrong with their father and it was going to be up to him to become the man of the house. Desperate times called for desperate measures and 'the Forty Thieves of Canning Town', as they had become known, were experts at petty larceny on the streets. The gang's name had been copied – out of respect – from that of the female crime syndicate led by Mary Carr whose exploits in the thieving business daily filled the newspaper columns. Queen Thief Mary gained her first conviction at the age of fourteen and had been coined *one of the most dangerous women in London*. With the help of the Elephant and Castle criminal gang, she formed the Forty Elephants. Her lawless band of young women plundered sophisticated West End shops, filling hidden, capacious pockets in their clothing with jewellery and other treasures. They became notorious for the fortunes they made and for the extravagant lifestyles they enjoyed as a result.

Bill knew what he was doing was wrong, and worried about being thrown into jail if he got caught, but decided it was worth the risk to keep the family out of the workhouse. Introducing Ernie to the game wasn't something he wanted to do, particularly if it involved violence, but the need for extra money was a constant problem. Lifting pouches of Golden Virginia from Butler's tobacco shop was an easy first challenge for the apprentice. Ernie passed with flying colours and, trusting his older brother implicitly, didn't question the more serious crime they were now undertaking. Sitting on the top of an alley wall after dark with their faces covered, they waited for an unsuspecting cyclist to come along. It was Bill's job to chuck a brick, knocking the rider off. Stealing the stunned victim's wallet and pocket watch was easy pickings, leaving Ernie to throw a 'Pedlar' punch, winding the poor man just long enough to enable them to make a clean getaway.

Unlike their female heroines, the Forty Thieves of Canning Town didn't get rich from their crimes – the majority of the gang being youngsters like Bill and Ernie. But for a while, at least, they managed to keep their families above the breadline.

'I'll tell you what,' said Bill, brushing the dirt off his cap. 'Let's go down Rathbone market and see if the muffin man's still there. Then we'll get jellied eels for everyone's tea.'

'I've got a spare tanner for the fortune-teller,' agreed Ernie, rummaging in his pockets. ''Opefully she'll tell us Pa's gunna get a better job then we won't 'ave to do this no more.'

FRIDAY, 26TH FEBRUARY 1904

Buttoning her old coat, Sarah followed the landlord down the short street past half a dozen derelict houses before stopping outside a six-roomed house in very bad repair.

'I'm letting it as two half-houses,' he declared. 'Upstairs is vacant – see what you think.'

Sarah made her way past dripping walls with peeling paper to the staircase. A quick glance back at the downstairs rooms revealed that the tenants had only sacks for bedding and they'd been well chewed by vermin. Upstairs was just as bad: clouds of flies were buzzing round every room. Horrified that she was going to be expected to pay three shillings a week to live in such squalor, Sarah told the man she wasn't interested and hurried away.

'You won't find nothing better,' he called out to her, shoving his hands in his pockets. 'Not in the *Marsh*, anyways. No one wants to live here no more.' Then as an afterthought, he added, '…Except those that have to.'

During Thames Iron Works' heyday, when the company had numerous ships on the stocks at the same time, the streets running along the side of the railway on the east side of Victoria Dock Road were in a better state – inhabited by mechanics and skilled men who had more money in their pockets. Since that time, the houses had degenerated mainly because they were built on marshland, at the same level as the Thames. Landlords were under no compulsion to make repairs if the rent was in arrears and as it usually was, nothing got done.

Passing the paraffin man and the usual coster barrows lining the side of the road, muddy water lapping around their wheels, Sarah played with the half-crown in her pocket. She'd meant to get some paraffin for the children's nits but that could wait; she'd just had a shock, so no one could deny her *one* drink in the Duke of Cambridge before getting the family's supper. Unsurprisingly, once inside the warm bar, it was all too easy to drown her fears in Old Tom gin thinking about Joseph and mulling over the plight of the family. It didn't take long before she'd lost track of the time and was in danger of spending the last thrupenny bit she'd need for a pound of kippers and her weekly penny dreadful.

No one thought much of Sarah, and she knew it. As a mother, being seen to squander precious shillings on drink went down far worse than when Joseph did the same. She'd got used to the way the family looked down their noses at her, especially her father-in-law's new wife, but even her own two sisters had long since given up on her. Thankfully they still did what they could for her children, although Nance had little time, seeing as she had the shop to contend with now that Sam wasn't as fit as he had been. Luckily, Fred, Harry and Joe had been enrolled at Clarkson Street School, where they were entitled to free dinners and an annual pair of boots. There were no handouts when Bill and Ernie were of an age to attend elementary, so it was well worth sending their younger brothers. Free or not, though, Sarah was quick to notice that a hole had been punched through the side of their boots in case of an attempt to pawn or sell them.

Desperate for money, Joseph had resorted to the workhouse labour yard for outdoor relief. Digging the infirmary grounds on a day when he felt able brought in just two shillings and twelve pounds of day-old bread. Sarah had no choice but to take on home work, so she asked Nellie and Norah Toy to put her in touch with their middleman.

John Toy had scrimped and saved for months to be able to buy his sisters a sewing machine and a fancy tally iron to enable them to join the thousand other West Ham women who made up clothing at home. The girls worked for one of the small shirt-making workshops in Upton which had sprung up in residential areas where there was a ready source of employees. Like most women in the Tidal Basin, Norah had started with the lowest class of work – making up slop shirts. It was an unpleasant task owing to the cheap material being full of lime, causing her eyes to smart and nose to run. Working in a room with no ventilation was awful, as everything quickly became covered in white dust. Things had improved now that she was making flannel shirts for which she got one shilling and ninepence a dozen. Being a quick worker, so long as she kept at it from seven in the morning till eight at night, she could bring in six shillings a week. Nellie earned much the same, providing she didn't burn her fingers shaping the fiddly collars.

There was no way that Sarah could afford a sewing machine like the Toy's Singer, so she took on the job of a finisher. Embarking on her first batch of shirts, she soon realised she'd have to work all hours of the day and night to earn anything like the kind of money the girls were earning. Buttoning and barring only paid tuppence per dozen shirts and, with seven buttons on each, it took an age to stitch the buttonholes sufficiently to pass the scrutiny of the pernickety middleman. In desperation, she'd turned to sewing up sacks as the only sensible option left open to her.

The alcohol having done the trick, Sarah left the Duke of Cambridge full of bravado. She'd made up her mind that there was nothing else for it but to beg Henry for money. Surely he wouldn't let his grandchildren live in one of those filthy houses she'd just been to? There was hardly a family on the Marsh that hadn't lost a child to typhoid and they'd already had a taste of how quickly disease spread when Lily got ill. Sarah was convinced it was diphtheria and the girl would end up all alone in the isolation hospital by the sewage works. Since no medical practitioner lived anywhere near the lowly Cyprus Estate, they'd had to beg Doctor Beaumont, who had a posh house in Winsor Terrace, to come down. The old Scotsman diagnosed a bad dose of measles and charged one shilling and sixpence – which they still owed him.

If that wasn't enough, she would show her father-in-law the cuts on her hands made by the tar rope and coarse needles used to sew up the sacks. She'd tell him she was working as hard as she could – five solid hours every day, which wasn't bad for a woman with a large brood to look after. But he needed to know that the 250 sacks she produced every week only brought in four shilling and tuppence, which just wasn't enough. And if he didn't believe she was pulling her weight, he was welcome to come and see for himself the bundles of sacks with her earnings scribbled on the attached tickets. In fact, it was about time that Henry came to the house to see how strangely Joseph was behaving and realise that his son was more to blame for their dire state than she was.

Henry Cook Pridmore stood in the doorway of the upstairs makeshift kitchen at 54 Lawrence Street and studied his son. Up till now he'd believed Joseph when he told him that his loss of regular earnings was down to modernisation in the docks, but there was clearly more to it than that. Sarah had talked of his insomnia, headaches and dizziness, but now Henry could see that he was acting more like an old man, mumbling and stammering and then forgetting what he'd just said. He seemed oblivious to his family's plight, talking instead of his plan to become landlord of the Ferndale, which he felt sure would become vacant soon, thereby enabling them to move back to Cyprus Place.

Convinced that returning to the familiar ground of Cyprus was a good idea, Henry agreed to pay the rent on some vacant upstairs rooms at 10 Beaconsfield Street until his son's health improved. He knew it wouldn't take long before Joseph was barred from the Ferndale again – which was, frankly, all to the good – but at least Nance would look out for the children.

Sarah's eyes lit up on hearing the news, and for the first time, Henry felt sorry for her. She was physically broken, her figure and looks gone through constant childbirth and alcohol. The only problem Henry now faced was convincing his own wife he'd made the right decision to help them. It was certainly going to be a challenge.

WEDNESDAY, 15TH JUNE 1904

'Come on, Ernie, keep running. They ain't taking us...' Bill and his brother clambered over the back wall and pelted down the alley.

'Better stay 'ere, until they've gone,' he whispered, grabbing Ernie's arm to stop him emerging out into Stanley Street. 'They might come looking for us.' Neither of them dared to move or speak until they heard an engine start up and then gradually fade away as it turned out of Beaconsfield Street.

'Do you think it's our fault?' asked Ernie, head bowed.

'What d'ya mean?' Bill said, scraping what smelt like dog mess off the side of his boot.

'Could it 'ave been someone we nicked from who shopped us all?'

'Don't be daft, we've been careful not to do any nicking round 'ere. Trust me, Ern, this is nothing to do with us.'

Ernie nodded, trying to hold back welling tears. 'I wonder what'll 'appen to the others. I was that close to grabbing Joe.'

'Nothing we could do, Ern. We 'ad to scarper when we got the chance, you know that. Joe wouldn't 'ave kept quiet and then we'd 'ave been carted off like the rest of 'em.'

Bill put a protective arm round his younger brother, and they started walking, instinctively in the direction of their aunt and uncle in Cyprus Place.

''Ave Ma and Pa gone too?'

'Reckon so, they were in a right old state. You saw what 'e'd done to the room. Tore it to shreds. Never seen 'im in such a rage. Only way to look at it, Ern, is that the girls'll get fed now.'

Ernie had indeed seen what his father had done and had been shocked to the core. Living with his parents was like a game of snakes and ladders. Something would go right and they'd climb one rung up the ladder, only to slide right to the bottom again straight after. But through it all, he'd never thought badly of his pa. He'd heard his ma and Aunt Nance talking of men who'd regularly come home from work and beat their wives and children. He'd seen women in the shop with a black eye or bruised nose and guessed how they'd got them. No one ever asked. And although he vaguely remembered what happened to Rosetta Sawkins over her broken window, Ernie was certain that his pa never raised a hand to his ma and he only ever gave any of his boys a good hiding when they deserved it. That was all most kids like him ever hoped or wished for. No, this was like nothing Ernie had seen before.

At nine that morning the authorities had come and taken away Fred aged ten, Harry eight, Joe six, Lily four, Betsy three and Ada at barely two. They were admitted to West Ham Union workhouse at Leyton with their mother and father. Bill and Ernie had hid behind a door when they saw their siblings being marched or carried down the stairs. Two burly men were restraining their father while a woman orderly, in a crisp apron and scraped-back hair, fended off their mother's abuse. The ensuing commotion gave them their chance to escape through the back-bedroom window. Sliding down the roof of the outhouse, they were in the yard in seconds.

The situation had become hopeless. Joseph's mood had been swinging alarmingly between euphoria and depression. For a lot of the time he was convinced he was wealthy. Full of his latest *successful* money-making scheme, he'd been promising to buy everyone drinks to celebrate. Sam had tried in vain to stop him doing it, while Sarah was hiding whatever money she earned. She'd learned the hard way, watching him squander a week's bread and milk money on drinking sessions like this. It was difficult to know which mood her husband was going to be in each day. When he wasn't elated and full of self-importance, he'd be racked with guilt over the family's misfortune, sitting silently in a state of despair. Other times he'd be violent and destructive. Either way, he'd stopped bringing in a wage and Sarah had pawned all their possessions, including her wedding ring.

Ernie fought back his tears as Bill spilled out the traumatic events of the morning. They'd done a bunk just in time and hiding out in the alley seemed the only way to avoid being taken into the workhouse. Neither Nance nor Sam could say they were surprised. Sarah had been drinking even more heavily over the past few weeks, no longer able to cope with her husband. It had become impossible to get any sense in or out of her. No one – including Henry – had the space, or the money, to keep the family together. Both Polly and Nance were at their wits' end constantly finding their bedraggled nephews and nieces on their doorsteps. All the little ones had sores round their mouths and crusts round their eyes. Wandering the streets malnourished with their older brothers thieving just to feed them, it was inevitable that someone would alert the authorities.

Bill and Ernie slept with their cousin George that night while his parents mulled over what to do with them.

'We can't turn 'em out, Sam,' Nance whispered, unable to sleep.

'No, I know,' he replied. 'They can live 'ere. Anything to get 'em away from those 'ooligan gangs in Canning Town. I'll see about getting Bill a job.'

Sandwiched between the other two boys, Ernie stared at the ceiling for a while before falling asleep. The image of veins bulging out of his father's neck as he was frogmarched out of the house would haunt him forever.

SUNDAY, 7ᵀᴴ AUGUST 1904

Nance spotted her sister first. It had only been a few weeks, but she'd grown quite thin and looked forlorn and embarrassed garbed in her workhouse clothes. On alternate Sundays, up to sixty inmates were allowed out to visit relatives, and today was Sarah's turn. Sitting on the grass with Fred and Harry, her face lit up when she saw her other sons coming towards her. Bill and Ernie squirmed as she stood up and tried to kiss them, but luckily Nance produced a big bag of clove rock and coconut ice just at the right time, and everyone settled down on the grass to enjoy it. Rubbing his sticky fingers on his trousers, Ernie found it hard not to stare at his brothers. They looked like twins with their cropped heads and matching institution uniforms.

'I couldn't bring all the children,' said Sarah, shielding her eyes from the bright afternoon sun. 'The little ones are alright – they're tucked away. It's Fred and 'arry who get the worst of it.' The sisters flashed knowing glances at one another, which didn't go unnoticed by Bill. Out of his pocket, he produced a grubby tennis ball. 'Come on, boys,' he said, stroking their bare heads. 'Let's go and 'ave a game.' Harry, who had been quiet up till now, jumped up and raced after his older brothers. Fred grabbed the last piece of confectionary and scoffed it quickly. 'We only get bread and skilly,' he laughed, licking the sugar off his lips as he ran to join the others.

Finding a broken branch that made a perfect bat, Ernie thought their game of cricket magical. He couldn't remember when the four brothers last had such a carefree time.

'Did you see much of our pa?' Bill asked Fred when it was their turn to be fielders.

'Not much,' he answered, shrugging his shoulders. 'We only got together once a week, and Ma and Pa wasted most of the time rowing. The girls loved being able to sit on 'is lap, though. I 'oped 'e'd get better, but 'e didn't and now 'arry cries all the time.'

'They won't be able to play for long,' said Sarah wistfully as she watched her boys. 'We 'ave to be back for 'alf past five. I'll be manning the drying 'orses till bedtime.'

Nance squeezed her sister's red and chapped hands, a dozen questions whirling round her head.

'The place is bursting at the seams, Nance. I can see dozens of paupers, just like me, queuing at the door. If we leave, I've been told we won't be "offered the house" a second time. I'll end up carrying the banner, and I can't do that to the kiddies. No, just 'ave to see what 'appens.'

Nance knew that 'carrying the banner' meant walking the streets all night. Locked out of parks and driven out of doors and passages by the police, it was what the homeless had to do. She also understood what Sarah meant by her last sentence.

It was already half a century since the union workhouse system had been introduced with the deliberate intention of making life inside them so unrelenting that people would do anything rather than be sent there. Things had changed very little, save that orphaned children, the elderly and infirm now received basic support rather than blame for their circumstances. But the stigma still remained.

A distraught Polly had hidden away from the neighbours in shame when her own sister, husband and children were admitted to the West Ham Union Workhouse. Since it opened, two thousand adults and over three hundred infants had passed through its doors – admissions doubling in the previous ten years alone. Standing outside the huge, unnerving building a few days later, she and Jim scanned the airing grounds in the vain hope of spotting the children. They didn't tarry long, though, the chiselled stone plaque over the entrance gate reminding them of what it meant to be destitute: *If any would not work, neither should he eat.* It sent shivers down their spines.

Joseph had squeezed his wife's hand as they were ushered into separate buildings, destined to see one other for just an hour a week after Sunday service. This applied to the children too, all of whom had to be scrubbed clean and have their heads de-loused with vinegar and lard. From her receiving ward, Sarah was eventually shown to a dormitory containing three dozen beds with barely enough room to stand between them. Changing into her drab, brown dress and bonnet, she was soon sent off to begin the relentless task of washing pots and pans with soda crystals in one of the huge kitchen sinks. Cleanliness, tidiness and joylessness were now the order of her day.

Initially assigned to maintaining the workhouse water-pumping system, Joseph's elaborate stories and mood swings soon got him in trouble. He'd be regaling his team with fictitious memories of his time as a professional boxer who had travelled to America and beaten the best they could offer, then promising to buy gifts with his winnings or threatening to go ten rounds with each of them. His youngest children, Joseph Junior and the girls, were placed in the nursery, but those over the age of seven were put with the adults – boys with the men, girls with the women. At mealtimes, Fred and Harry had to sit in rows facing the same way and adhere to the strict rule of silence in the dining room. They ate as fast as they could, terrified in case their father would shout out or ramble incessantly, as he was prone to do. His outbursts frequently cost him twenty-four-hour stints on bread and water and the loss of his weekly, one-ounce tobacco ration. It didn't take long for the job on the pumps to be taken away from him and be relegated to breaking stones or the picking shed. With room for ninety offenders and vagrants, picking oakum – unpicking old rope and remaking it – was an occupation that resulted in raw and cut hands.

Following bouts of elation and mania, Joseph suffered days of deep depression – days when he'd beg for alcohol to steady his nerves. He'd yell about being no use to his wife and how he'd be better off dead. On one such day he somehow managed to totter out of the workhouse unseen and disappear deep into the wetland on Beckton Marshes. Had it been winter he would certainly have died there, but a marshman, vaulting over ditches on his jumping pole, spotted his emaciated body, half buried in the thick mud. Knowing a gypsy camp was nearby, the marshman got one of their boys to use his horse to drag Joseph out. With no signs of life during the rescue, both were mightily surprised to find the senseless man still breathing.

Wrapped in a blanket and still holding a length of rope he'd brought with him, the rescued man remained eerily quiet as he was transported on a flat-bed cart back to the workhouse, where an examination of his physical and mental state was carried out. Taking into account his recent behaviour and this latest episode which had nearly cost him his life, the medical officer was in no doubt that Joseph was no longer of sound mind and body, writing in his casebook: *Diagnosis – mania with general paralysis, prognosis unfavourable.* With no further ado, once suitable transportation had arrived, he escorted his patient to the Pauper Lunatic Asylum for the County of Essex, South Weald, near Brentwood.

No one knew for sure whether Joseph had been intending to commit suicide, but under the circumstances it was a fair assumption. Soon the story was circulating around Cyprus that he *had* killed himself on the marshes. Some of the Ferndale customers who'd had dealings with him in the past received the news with ghoulish interest, whilst others shied away, respectful of his wider family living only doors away.

Sam was shocked to the core that his brother could have ended up in such a state and withdrew into himself. Nance was different – stronger, maybe – and, once she'd absorbed the gravity of the situation, quickly turned her attention to disguising the truth from her nephews.

'Fred and 'arry think their father passed away in the work'ouse,' she told her husband after meeting Sarah. 'I think it's best if Bill and Ernie carry on believing 'e died on the marshes. We can't deny that the poor devil went there – they've 'eard it said too many times. It's got to be better than knowing 'e's locked up in a lunatic asylum and never likely to see the light of day again.'

Reluctantly, Sam agreed. He knew they might find out the truth one day, but with Bill now running messages around the Albert Dock and Ernie helping out in the shop whilst learning to read and write, keeping them settled was all that mattered.

Joseph Pridmore

WEDNESDAY, 2ND NOVEMBER 1904

The stock of old wardrobes and broken timbers had cleared quite quickly once word of Henry selling up had gone round St Luke's Square. It was a great relief knowing that there wasn't much left to shift, as it helped relieve the tension behind the scenes. Maud had kept out of the shop since the family were taken into the workhouse and the dreadful news about Joseph had led to an ultimatum. She was going back to Wisbech with or without him.

Henry had no regrets as he prised off the makeshift sign over the front door. With a final glance at the words *Pridmore, dealer in marine stores*, he hurled the rough piece of wood on top of a pile of mouldy canvas and sailcloth dumped down the side alley. Brushing the dust off his moustache and waistcoat, he leaned against the lamppost and looked across at St Luke's, where he'd gone to pray after being told where his son had been found. It hadn't done any good; in fact, things had got worse. He'd been to the asylum and seen a catatonic Joseph lying motionless on the floor under his bed. Now haunted by the image, he was having sleepless nights. Maud had reminded her husband that he was getting on in years and all the worrying was taking its toll on his own health. He couldn't disagree and had recognised it was time they looked after themselves.

'So you're really going, Pa,' said Eliza, switching her baby daughter from one hip to the other. The shop looked much bigger now that it was nearly empty and badly in need of decorating. ''Arold could do this place up a treat,' she laughed as Henry swept the dust into the corner. All that was left by way of furniture was an old chest lacking a drawer and all of its handles, and a horsehair chair with a six-inch rent in its seat. 'We'll take them off your 'ands,' she added eagerly.

'I hope you're going to be alright,' Henry said, taking little Grace from her mother. 'I have my doubts about that Harold Pike. You sure he's going to stand by you?'

'Well, 'e 'as so far. I got no choice but to stay with 'im now, Pa, 'ave I?'

Henry nodded; there wasn't much more to say since Grace, now nearly three months old, was Eliza's third child to have been born out of wedlock. The father was a painter and decorator whom no one thought very bright but at least earned a few shillings a week doing up rooms for a property landlord in Wanstead. Henry was concerned that, despite calling herself Eliza Pike so that their child would have that name too, they were not married. With no legal responsibility, Harold Pike could throw Eliza out if he had a mind to and then this child would end up like the others.

'I'll be at the baptism on Friday,' said Henry, pushing his doubts aside. 'Then Maud and me'll be off back to Wisbech. More than my life's worth if I don't go.'

SATURDAY, 30TH SEPTEMBER 1905

Suffering from physical and mental exhaustion, having lost all power of locomotion and no longer able to feed himself, Joseph drifted into a paralytic coma after which death came swiftly. His suffering had lasted nine months, during which time he had fought all medicine, asserting that he had never been so well – a claim which his hollow features and wasted body clearly denied.

Joseph's case wasn't unusual. It was mirrored in asylums across Britain, with hundreds of men in their thirties and forties receiving the diagnosis of *General Paralysis of the Insane*. Seldom occurring in females, it was widely regarded as the result of a debauched and intemperate life. Many doctors suspected that it was the outcome of untreated syphilis and that, in its final stage, sometimes fifteen to twenty years after infection, it attacked the brain, rendering its victims helpless. Prognosis was bleak, most dying within months or weeks after admission. The social effects of the disease were felt acutely in families, since it attacked men in the prime of life who were also the breadwinners. When, in 1905, the bacterium *Treponema pallidum* was finally proven to be the link between general paralysis and syphilis; it was sadly just too late for Joseph.

Sam waited bareheaded by the unmarked grave as the wind whistled through the trees, blowing the early-autumn leaves in circles around him. Standing alongside his brother's coffin, he felt despondent and alone. It took just minutes for the two gravediggers to lower it into its final resting place and for the minister to throw in a handful of soil whilst uttering the all-too-familiar words. Then it was all over. Without further ado, the three men left, leaving Sam to walk dejectedly home. Cold and impersonal as it was, it could have been so much worse, he thought.

Coming from the workhouse, it was assumed that Joseph deserved no more than a pauper's burial. It wasn't unusual for twelve coffins to be piled on top of one another in a mass grave without any kind of ceremony. But Sam wasn't having that. He had forked out a guinea for the funeral and a further two shillings to the gravediggers to allow his brother to be buried with a modicum of dignity. It may have cost a week's worth of shop takings but was the right thing to do. Like it or not, he and Nance would have to cut down on their spending for a while to make up for the loss.

Families would go without food and warmth to avoid the shame of a pauper's burial. They scrimped to take out a penny insurance policy, to cover funeral costs, each time a new child came along. Unfortunately, Sam discovered that once Joseph stopped working, his payments lapsed, and such was the unfairness of the system that all his benefits were lost.

MONDAY, 19TH FEBRUARY 1906

Polly Lear almost collapsed with relief on hearing Daisy using the foot scraper by the front door. She'd been pacing the floor for most of the day, worried stiff that her daughter might have got herself arrested. She was only seventeen and the image of her being slapped in handcuffs and carted off to a police station just wouldn't go away.

'Oh, Ma, I told you not to worry,' Daisy assured her as her toes gradually thawed out by the heat of the range. 'They can't stop us marching and it was such an important day.' Having just taken part in the first ever London march of the Women's Social and Political Union, Daisy was still riding the wave of excitement it had created. 'There were *two 'undred* of us from Bow, Canning Town and Poplar. We marched to Caxton Hall first, then when we 'eard there was no mention of votes for women in the King's Speech, Mrs Pankhurst led everyone on to the opening of Parliament. "The women were awake at last," she said. It was so inspiring, Ma – Mrs Pankhurst 'ad us all cheering and clapping.'

Her mother feigned some understanding of the suffragette movement but really knew nothing of politics, nor wanted to. Suspicious of the activists' motives at Silver's Rubber Works, where Daisy was a factory hand, Polly was sure she'd picked up her ideas there and that ultimately no good would come of it.

Truth was, she didn't understand why women should want the vote. Jim had it and that was enough for her. Most of the men working as casuals in the docks weren't entitled because you had to have been at the same address for twelve months. Anyway, Polly couldn't see women ever being considered equal – not that she objected to them marching and handing out leaflets – but resorting to violence in support of the cause just didn't seem right.

Ever since Christabel Pankhurst had got herself arrested a few months back, the newspapers had changed their tune and were now more critical than supportive. It didn't bode well. Polly comforted herself with the thought that her eldest daughter would be married soon and wouldn't have time for protesting about the vote, or anything else for that matter.

Daisy Lear had always known her own mind. It was probably why she'd left such an impression on her cousin Ernie when they were growing up. It was usually Daisy out of all the Lear children who was in trouble and the one that Ernie went looking for down the back alleys. Not wanting anyone to see her crying, she'd stay in hiding until she was able to calm down. Ernie would do his best to speed that up by playing a tune on an old harmonica he always carried in his pocket. Pulling a face or doing a jig at the same time would turn her sobs to laughter and eventually they'd go back inside. All children knew their place and failing to show respect for a father's authority would often result in a beating. Not that Jim would ever go that far, but his sons often got a clip round the ear. In Daisy's case, being cheeky would result in a slap on the back of the leg, which Jim looked to Polly to administer.

Knowing that she was never going to bring her mother round to her way of thinking, Daisy went to help her younger sister Mary stir the stew in readiness for their father and brother William to return from the gas works. Alf was sitting happily in the corner looking at the cartoons in a copy of *Comic Cuts*. Nearly nineteen now, his behaviour was far less agitated than in the past.

As Polly watched her younger children happily playing Ludo, she considered herself extremely lucky. There was nothing she would change. As long as Jim was able to work and they could stay in their own home in Bradley Street, she was content. Most women would be, if they'd found a good, solid man who kept their families clothed and fed. But with so much unemployment these days, there was chronic poverty in the Tidal Basin. Desperate women like her unfortunate sister were everywhere. It was hardly surprising that they couldn't cope.

Within days of Joseph's death the previous October, Sarah had signed all the paperwork, collected her own clothes and walked out of the workhouse, leaving her six children behind. Polly was shocked to the core when she opened her front door and found her standing there.

'I can't stay around 'ere, Poll,' she'd replied curtly when asked what she intended to do. 'Nor can I go back to Cyprus Place. Everyone'll blame me for leaving the children behind – but I can't look after 'em, I've got nothing. Besides, I only ever saw 'em on Sundays. It's been over a year and the girls 'ardly know me.'

'But what about Bill and Ernie? Surely you'll want to see them before you go?' pleaded Polly.

'They're nicely settled with Nance and Sam, and besides, Bill's earning 'is keep now.' Sarah took a final gulp of tea, put the cup down and fixed her sister with a determined look. 'No, I shan't go there – best to let sleeping dogs lie. I need to earn money and find somewhere to live. Look, Poll, that's why I've come 'ere. Can you see your way to giving me a few bob so I can get to Spitalfields? There's a Jewish tobacconist on Commercial Street that's willing to take me in so long as I cook and clean for 'is family.'

Polly barely recognised the emotionless woman sitting before her asking for a handout and it was clear nothing was going to make her change her mind. She wondered what Jim was going to say about the missing rain-day money while stretching for the old tobacco tin under her mattress.

A week later, Polly informed Nance of their sister's visit. Between them they decided this was going to be another secret they'd keep from Bill and Ernie – in fact, they pledged not to talk of her again. Often in the middle of the night, though, Polly would go back over the past. Although close as children, their lives had gone down such different paths and it would have been easy to blame Sarah's drinking on Joseph, but she knew better. They were both flawed and that's why they had such a disastrous marriage. Whichever way you looked at it, there really wasn't any alternative to the family going into the workhouse and although everyone thought badly of Sarah leaving the children behind, Polly didn't know what else she could have done. Given the alternatives, maybe they were in the best place.

TUESDAY, 8TH MAY 1906

Finding out that Henry Pridmore had shut his marine stores and gone back to Wisbech left Amelia Bateman in a quandary as to how to locate his daughter Eliza. No one at Clarkson Street seemed to know where she'd gone, so her only hope was to head for Cyprus Place to find her brother Sam.

After breakfast, Amelia had done her best to make John look presentable, fussing a little too much over his wayward hair, before making their way to Canning Town station. John studied the worn-out faces of the men on the busy workman's train to the gas works, wondering why he'd been taken out of school for such an adventure. Not that he was complaining, especially when it meant being introduced to his uncle and aunt and cousin George, who owned a *sweet shop*.

With eyes as big as saucers, John surveyed the array of tempting jars, unable to believe his luck. No sooner had they arrived that he was told he could have two ounces of bonbons and bullseyes. Just so long as he and George went outside, to leave the adults to talk.

With both boys being only eight, they didn't have much to say to one another, so George was relieved when Ernie appeared round the corner.

'I'll just wash me sticky 'ands and then we can go and 'ave a kickabout,' Ernie said, lifting his cap to wipe the sweat off his brow after a long day at the bottling stores. 'Too nice an evening to 'ang around 'ere.' It wasn't long before the boys were kicking a well-worn football along Cyprus Place, Ernie demonstrating the skills of his old West Ham hero Charlie Dove.

'So you're not brothers then?' John enquired as they arrived at the Savage Garden allotments and immediately lost the football in a crop of someone's cabbages.

'Nah, we're cousins,' Ernie replied, retrieving the ball and dribbling it along the narrow footway. 'I think of 'im as me little brother, though. Even if 'e 'as got two left feet,' he added, as George tripped up attempting a tackle.

'So 'ave you got no ma and pa like me?'

'Ern's dad's dead and 'is mum's left all 'is younger brothers and sisters in the work'ouse,' George growled, picking himself up off the ground. 'That's why 'e lives with us.'

Ernie flashed him a look. He didn't need anyone answering for him.

'I live with the Batemans,' continued John. 'Been there since I was a baby, but I know my name is Pridmore just like you two.'

'Sounds like I'm the only one with their proper ma and pa then,' declared George with a superior air and not daring to catch Ernie's eye. 'I've 'ad enough of this, I'm going 'ome. Make sure you bring *my* ball back when you come.'

Letting off some steam, Ernie kicked the treasured object rather too hard and it landed in the next allotment. A man earthing up potatoes retrieved it and threw it back along with a few choice swearwords. Calling it a day, Ernie guided John down the short cuts of the Cyprus estate towards the shop with their surname above the door. All too soon, it seemed, Amelia Bateman and her foster child were bidding their farewells.

'Did we do the right thing?' asked Nance as she and Sam watched Amelia help John clamber onto a tram with Eliza's address in her purse.

'Without doubt,' Sam replied. 'But she'll be wasting 'er time. My sister won't want 'im back, I'm quite sure about that.'

Ernie mulled over the events of the day as he waited for his steaming plate of tripe and onions to cool. He'd taken an instant liking to young John. The boy was easy-going, bright and funny. No one had explained why Mrs Bateman had brought him over and it clearly was a surprise, as Aunt Nance said she hadn't seen him since he was handed over as a baby. Ernie knew that John's real mother was Eliza and that she'd had more children, but he hadn't dared say anything about that. It was bound to come out in the wash soon enough. What niggled him most were George's put-downs and rubbing it in that he was the poor relation. Things were going to change, though – that was definite.

Sam had got Bill a proper job sticking labels on bottles at M. B. Foster & Sons, beer and cider merchants in North Woolwich. With their own wharf, they were the largest exporter of Bass in the world. At fourteen, Ernie started there too. It was a monotonous job, but he was earning six shillings and sixpence a week, two shillings less that his brother. After paying Nance for their board and lodging, Bill religiously put his extra two shillings into savings. He vowed that as soon as there was enough, they were going to get their siblings out of the workhouse, find somewhere to live and be a family once more.

SUNDAY, 24TH JUNE 1906

It had taken quite a while to dock the huge SS *Kensington* in the harbour. Amelia Bateman stood on the deck, hardly daring to believe her eyes as the great city of Montreal spread out in front of her. Not that this was the end of her journey; it was going to be another two days by train before reaching Winnipeg, and then even more hours to Bowsman.

With five of her children in tow, most of her Tidal Basin neighbours thought she was mad to embark on a new life at her age, especially in the wilds of Canada. Lord knows what we'll find when we get to the farmstead, she thought. Someone she'd been talking to on deck told her it was a marshland. They'd both laughed and said, 'Not much different to Canning Town, then.'

The truth is they had no choice other than to give it a try. Her sons had been to the Salvation Army's Hadleigh Farm Colony in Essex which had been turned over to train boys in preparation for agricultural jobs overseas. They just had to hope it was enough to deal with whatever lay ahead. Anyway, they weren't alone. The ship was full of broken families just like hers.

Amelia could pinpoint the event that had changed everything for them. In late November 1904 her husband Charlie had gone to watch Woolwich Arsenal play a match against Everton. He'd come home late complaining of the 'pea-souper' that had caused the game to be abandoned in the second half. Smog had descended onto the pitch so thickly that you could only gauge the whereabouts of the ball when a spectator spotted it and cheered. Then, to add insult to injury, he'd had to abandon his omnibus and walk home.

The treacherous smog lay like a blanket throughout December, causing the docks to grind to a halt. Suddenly, everyone was in dire straits, including Amelia's adult sons. Then, as if things weren't bad enough, her husband suffered a fatal accident in the chemical factory and died just before Christmas.

With ships waiting outside the docks, attention was called to the condition of West Ham by several of the daily newspapers. Launching charitable campaigns to raise extra relief funds, some handed over money to the clergy and public men to distribute where they thought best, others set up committees to give out groceries and coal directly from the Town Hall. Works schemes, such as paving recreation grounds and painting the East London Hospital, were set up by the *Daily News*, but the *Daily Telegraph* turned its attention to emigration as a more permanent solution to the problem.

Assisted emigration had begun in earnest in 1903, with the Salvation Army working hard to enable families from all over the country to start a new life in the rural parts of Ontario and Manitoba. With its much-publicised aim of bringing *the landless man to the manless land*, by 1905 there was sufficient demand for the Salvation Army to charter its own ship to carry one thousand people to Canada 'under the Army flag'.

The Daily Telegraph Shilling Fund raised £15,000 in its first year. In an unprecedented co-operative move, the Salvation Army and many other agencies and charities, worked together with the *Daily Telegraph* to send nearly four thousand people to Canada the following year – the Bateman family among them.

Eliza Pridmore had been horrified to see Amelia Bateman on the doorstep of 37 Cecil Road, Leytonstone, and hurried her inside. It was quickly established that taking John back was out of the question. Things were precarious enough with Harold Pike and, now that she was expecting again, he was already complaining there were too many mouths to feed. Amelia had tried to explain that as John's unofficial foster mother there would be questions asked if the family tried to take him to Canada, even assuming they were in a mind to do so, but it made no difference. Eliza hurried her away, begging her not to inform the authorities of her whereabouts.

With a heavy heart, Amelia left John Pridmore in the hands of the West Ham Union Workhouse. The official paperwork recorded that his grandfather now resided in Wisbech and his mother's whereabouts were unknown. The only crumb of comfort for Amelia was that his younger sister Rachel was already there, along with the six children of Eliza's brother Joseph. He wouldn't know any of them, but they all shared the same surname.

For the Batemans, walking down the gangplank of the *Kensington* alongside other anxious, excited immigrants, their future was hopeful. The children missed John and didn't understand why he had been left behind in West Ham. Amelia simply thanked God that they weren't still there too.

FRIDAY, 7TH MAY 1909

Ernie woke up, and for a split second didn't remember. Then it hit him like a steam train. Bill was dead. They'd found his body, so there was no longer any hope. Grief, loneliness, fury and bitterness surged through his veins – emotions he'd never experienced before, so raw that he could almost taste them.

Sam was already up and staring blankly out of the filthy window. He'd been to get the local newspaper and was back in the room they'd taken at the Old Falcon Hotel during the inquest.

'There's nothing more we can do 'ere, Ern,' he sighed, realising his nephew was now awake. 'Best we go 'ome.' Ernie nodded and was getting dressed when he saw the headline on an open page of the *Gravesend Reporter*:

The Thames Disaster

Yesterday (Thursday) morning a body was recovered from the river, just above the Deep Water Wharf, Northfleet, it having been discovered by Mr Charles Pilcher, a Northfleet waterman. Bringing it to the shore the Northfleet police were communicated with, and they recovered the body to the mortuary where it was subsequently identified as that of William Pridmore, of Woolwich, late second mate of the tug Britannia.

On the point of going to Press we learnt that Mr A Shuttlewood of 12 Church Street found a body near the

Ship and Lobster, and it was landed at Gravesend. It has been identified as that of Thomas. The body of Livett it is hoped will soon be found.

Meanwhile the sad catastrophe has formed the subject of general conversation, but the real circumstances, hitherto only speculated upon, were made known on Tuesday at the adjourned inquest on the bodies of Engineer Jeffery and leading Fireman Towe.

It had taken a while for the authorities to locate Bill's next of kin to inform them of the capsizing of his tug *Britannia* on the 24th April. At that stage some of the crew were still missing, presumed drowned, Bill amongst them. For worried relatives, waiting was the worst part. As the days went by, hopes of finding the men alive faded. An inquest was scheduled for Tuesday, 4th May at Gravesend Town Hall, which Sam and Ernie attended with heavy hearts. They listened intently to the tragic turn of events that had taken place in the early hours of that Saturday, after the steam tug *Britannia* set out from the Terrace Pier on a routine trip to the Royal Albert dock.

Captain James Curtiss, a freeman of the river with over forty years' experience, had been on the bridge with first mate Frank Box at the wheel. Posted forward on the deck was the second mate, William Pridmore. As they passed the entrance to Tilbury docks, the SS *Bazalgette*, a London County Council sewerage disposal vessel, approached, heading downstream. With a distance of some three quarters of a mile between the two, the larger *Bazalgette* appeared to manoeuvre to safely pass the tug when, apparently caught by the tide, her bow swung violently around, colliding with the *Britannia*. Struck broadside, the tug capsized almost immediately. The violent impact flung Curtiss and Box into the water, from where they were both rescued after a few minutes. However, there was no trace of the remainder of the crew. The stricken tug was raised the next morning. A diver entering the hull discovered the bodies of engineer George Jeffery and leading fireman Ernest Towe.

A great deal of evidence was given to establish the position of the two vessels just before impact, including what navigation lights were showing. Finally, the jury retired for their deliberation, returning just ten minutes later with a verdict of accidental death. The coroner suggested that the evidence was sufficient to show that no one was clearly to blame and therefore the deceased were accidently drowned in the collision. Frank Box stated that William Pridmore could only swim a few strokes and to his knowledge had not been in deep water before. Second fireman Ben Thomas was also a non-swimmer.

The following day, with still no news of Bill, Sam and Ernie made the decision to go and see the stricken *Britannia*. The vessel was now moored at Clifton Slipway supported by a large crane – her black funnel with its two white rings instantly recognisable. She was a sorry sight. Men were on board, already working on her superstructure. When Sam told one of them who they were, he immediately came ashore. Shaking them by the hand, he expressed his deep regret and spoke of how the disaster had affected everyone. Apparently, a large crowd had gathered when the *Britannia* was brought to the surface, their heads bowed in respect. Passing ships and boats had lowered their flags to half-mast. Ernie winced at the description of the two men the diver had found. The engineer had been pinned against an air pump by a large fragment of metal whilst the leading fireman, taking a rest in his cabin, had been caught unaware.

Thursday, 6th May brought the news that Sam had been dreading. Bill's body had been found, along with that of Ben Thomas. Sadly for the family of the ship's boy, Henry Levitt, there was still no trace. A policeman arrived to accompany Sam to the mortuary to formally identify his nephew. He knew that, on his return, he would be faced with the unenviable task of telling Ernie. Accepting the loss of his beloved brother was going to be unbearable.

Now, sitting in the bar of the Old Falcon, Sam downed a third brandy before taking a small brown paper package out of his pocket and passing it silently to his nephew. Inside was a damp handkerchief wrapped around Bill's pocket watch and chain.

In the days that followed, Gravesend and Northfleet echoed with the words of Canon Gedge, Rector of St George's Church, 'Since living in Gravesend I can remember nothing that would compare in sadness to this catastrophe.' To help compensate those affected, Rosherville Gardens was used for a benefit day, the proceeds of which were to go to the bereaved families. A school holiday was granted to all local children with a reminder as to its purpose, and the statutory half-day closing was altered to coincide with the benefit day.

On 12th May a grand matinee, *On behalf of the Sufferers of the recent sad Tug Disaster*, took place at the theatre in Harmer Street, celebrities giving their services for free. Ernie received a copy of the programme for the event which included a poem:

'Ere the daylight had wended its way through the skies;
'Ere the dismal rain ceased, came the tears to our eyes;
For the news we'd heard without warning
That the lives of five souls had been cast to the deep –
Maybe at their duties; maybe whilst asleep –
On that sad, ne'er forgot April morning,
How soon the news spread, though the hours were small,
Such news as we dread, and care not to recall,
For it fills every heart with emotion.
So sudden, not even a moment to spare,
Came the crash, then the cries of those in despair,
Fighting hard in the Thames' tidal motion,
'Tis but two of the party of seven survive.
Many thanks be to God that these two are alive
For the help that was near them that morn.
To the 'Bargee' great credit is due; and the way
Cory's lifeboat was manned 'tis but fair to say
British pluck still remains to be scorned.

The stricken tug Britannia, photographed by Messrs.
Daines Bros. Gravesend

SATURDAY, 24TH JULY 1909

The tragedy hit Nance particularly badly. She felt she was partly to blame for Bill's death seeing as it was her that had got him started on the river in the first place. It had been obvious that both brothers were going nowhere sticking labels on beer bottles. It's not that they ever complained. Tedious as the task was, they never missed a day or were late, but there were no prospects, and she knew that's what counted if they wanted to make something of themselves.

Thinking back to her first job as a servant girl in the home of a river pilot, Nance plucked up the courage to pay him a visit. Half expecting to be shooed away from the posh end of Plaistow, it had been a great relief to be welcomed inside his comfortable house. Now close to retirement, John Simmons listened intently to the description of two near-orphans who were not shy of hard work and had learned how to read and write and undertake basic maths without going to school. Her plea convinced him to give them a chance. He would have each one in turn for a year.

'Just for pocket money, mind, and there'll be plenty of splicing and scrubbing,' said Simmons with a wink. 'But they'll work beside me and learn well,' he added as Nance stood up to leave.

For Bill it had been a great success; the new deckhand had gone on to board the United Steam Tug Company's *Britannia* with his head held high – not least because Simmons had agreed to be his Master throughout his ongoing five-year apprenticeship to become a Freeman of the Company of Watermen and Lightermen of the River Thames.

Apprenticeships for licenses to work on the river were highly prized. As far back as the sixteenth century, it had been all too common for people to lose their lives as a result of the lack of skill and knowledge of the wherrymen and watermen. The Company of Watermen had been formed to regulate passenger-carrying on the Thames. Lightermen, who transported goods from ship to wharf, were later bound by the same regulations. By the nineteenth century the company had assumed wide-reaching authority over the Thames, including routes, fixing fares and registration of boats and barges.

So for Nance, when she watched Ernie step forward to sign his indenture papers two days before his eighteenth birthday, his equal success left her with mixed feelings. Although intensely proud of her nephew, she had felt a knot in the pit of her stomach. Bill had been a tuggie for barely nine months before he was drowned. Looking at John Simmons she thought she saw a tear in his eye too as he raised his pen to agree to be Ernie's Master for five years.

But no matter what fears Nance may have had for Ernie following in his brother's footsteps, there was no denying that such an opportunity would set him up for the future. He was now a deckhand on another United Steam Tug Company's vessel – the *Dunera*. With the newspapers full of reports about a new dock being built below the Albert, there were going to be even more ships requiring the expertise of a tug's crew to navigate the dangerous waters of the Thames Estuary, towing them upriver to their berths.

It was the Crimean War boom of the 1850s that changed the fortunes of steam tugs working the Thames. The sailing transports had to make three calls before they completed their loading – at Deptford for military stores, Woolwich for ammunition and Gravesend for their troops. They couldn't afford to wait for a favourable tide and winds to coincide, so the demand for tugs exceeded anything that had ever been seen before.

Wooden paddle-wheelers towed sailing ships in and out of port before iron-clad screw-tugs were introduced. Competition between ships at the end of their long voyages was acute. Time meant money, and demand for towing was at a premium.

There was also competition between the tug companies as improvements in the design and construction of their vessels meant they could travel a greater distance down the Channel to meet homeward-bound ships. The further they got the better chance there was of picking up a good job. The only restriction was coal. It was easy to go too far and be left without sufficient to get home, so it was often a game of cat and mouse between skippers as they tried to outwit their rivals in the practice known as 'seeking'. Being the first on site to rescue vessels in trouble was a lucrative part of it – a crew's portion of compensation for salvage was set at twenty per cent.

Of course, there could be days wasted in fruitless search, with a tug being out for weeks on end. The skipper would survive on occasional naps, until they struck lucky. Then, if the sea was calm enough to permit the tug to go alongside, he would jump on board and strike a bargain, but more often than not the business details were discussed at great length by shouting across the water.

This was what Bill had been looking forward to after completing his apprenticeship. It was going to take time before he rose up through the ranks. But it wasn't to be. Now it was his younger brother's turn and perhaps it was hardly surprising that everyone concerned had greeted the boy's promotion with a sense of trepidation.

Ernie lay on his bunk, too exhausted to bother about being soaking wet from the waist down. He was still fully dressed, save for his sea boots, which were strategically placed for his feet to slip straight into when he rose an hour or so later. High winds had made it a difficult tow, with the possibility of the tug being overrun, girded or even capsized. The deckhands needed to be careful not to get too near the towrope for fear that it would part.

The *Dunera* had been nicknamed the 'Switch-back Railway' due to her tendency to lift her stern and had to be run heavily ballasted to counteract this. She was only a small tug and the previous week, in similar weather conditions, had been unable to tow in a large ship. That time they had kept her engines going slow ahead to act as a sea anchor, the fireman keeping an eagle eye on their precious coal supply.

Accidents causing damage were all too frequent, so the ownership of vessels was split into shares as a way of sharing risk. The United Steam Tug Company was one of many Gravesend-based syndicates made up of tug masters, pilots and local businessmen. They painted two white rings on the black funnels of their new screw-tugs, which was how the fleet came to be known by its more common name of 'ring tugs'. The first of these was the *Durunda*. She came unstuck when towing a ship to Dunkirk in heavy seas, shedding her propeller off the Isle of Wight. The *Dunera* found her and towed her back to Gravesend.

Crews faced situations like this all the time. You might leave Gravesend at high water, fall in with a vessel off Margate and tow her to London within twenty-four hours. Other times you could be out a fortnight before finding one. The captain and engineer would be on duty all the time, the rest of the seven-man crew on twelve-hour watches. Then after just one night at home you'd have to be ready to start again.

In what seemed no time at all, Ernie's break was up. He put on his oil skins and instinctively lit a cigarette. It was the middle of the night and he was dog-tired but had come to an important decision. He would put Bill's benefit fund into a savings account for each of his three sisters. It was what his brother would have wanted.

Sam had been thinking about it too and, to thank the townsfolk for their generosity, sent a personal letter to the *Gravesend Reporter*:

GRATEFUL ACKNOWLEDGEMENTS
To the Editor
BRITANNIA FUND

Sir – I should esteem it a very great favour if you would convey through your paper, to the subscribers of the above fund, the sincere and heartfelt thanks of my family and myself for their great kindness in assisting us in our great trouble – yours very sincerely,

SAMUEL PRIDMORE (Uncle of William Pridmore)
17 Cyprus Place, New Beckton

WEDNESDAY, 20TH OCTOBER 1909

It was early July when John put his name to a piece of paper saying he agreed to go to Canada. In fact, he couldn't wait to go. They'd told the eleven-year-old that instead of being confined in a workhouse, he would be living on a farm, earning his keep out in the fresh air. To tackle the problems of childhood poverty, destitution and moral decline in London, thousands of children had already been despatched in this way. It had been going on for forty years.

Scottish Quaker Annie MacPherson had been so appalled by the state of children's lives in London's East End that she opened four homes, including the Spitalfields Home of Industry where children could be taught a trade. Those attending her night classes after work got a hot meal thrown in too. Though successful, it soon became evident to MacPherson and other philanthropists such as Thomas Barnardo, who were following her lead, that the scale of the problem required a more radical solution.

That solution was emigration. In 1870, Annie MacPherson started the Home Children Scheme and accompanied the first batch of orphans from London's workhouses to Canada. Receiving homes were built in Ontario and Quebec, and waifs and strays began to be sent on a monthly basis to work on farms and undertake domestic duties. Such was the uptake that seven applicants came forward for every child.

MacPherson died in 1904, handing responsibility for transporting more than five hundred children every year to her nephew William Merry. No one doubted their benevolent motives, but problems existed which were casting a shadow over the programme. What happened to the foundlings after placement was often poorly monitored and while some farmers genuinely cared for the boys, others just saw them as cheap labour. If a 'home child' was deemed unsuitable, they could be returned, which led to some having to be placed several times. Letters in the local newspapers talked of the *moral deterioration of Canadians resulting from the export of problem children to their shores.*

Back in England, John's group caught the attention of long-time labour champion and now MP for West Ham South, Will Thorne. Having discovered that the guardians of his local workhouse were sending children as young as eight overseas, he started putting pressure on the Government to halt their emigration. But the intervention came too late for John. He and twenty-six other orphans from the West Ham Union, and a further seventy-two from other London Unions, had already been assembled at the MacPherson's training home in London Fields, Hackney.

After being examined by a doctor – who seemed to pay particular attention to those with unappealing skin and eye diseases – John was passed fit for emigration, while four of those from West Ham, including his mate Robert, who had a face full of conspicuous sores, were removed from Mr Merry's list and sent back.

Without further ado, John packed his small two-by-one-foot wooden box with *Grand Trunk Railway, Miss MacPherson, Stratford Ontario Canada* painted on the side. With so few clothes, there was plenty of space for his precious tin soldier collection, passed down by the Bateman boys.

The party travelled to Liverpool Lime Street by train and then walked to Royal Albert Dock to board the Allan Line's SS *Tunisian*. John had seen plenty of ships this size in the Albert Dock at home, but now he was actually going on one. Despite being in steerage – and incredibly smelly – the four-berth emigrant cabins had spring mattresses and hot and cold running water. After life in the workhouse, it was pure luxury.

The *Tunisian* left Liverpool on the 29ᵗʰ July, breaking through the fog in the St Lawrence River nine days later. Baptist layman William Merry thanked God for such a calm crossing, with the entire group well enough to pass a further inspection on arrival in Quebec harbour. He led the children down the gangplank, clutching his manifest with the words *Desirable Class* stamped on it, and headed for the Grand Trunk Railway station. What he hadn't told the weary little ones was that it was to be another twelve hours before they would fall into bed at the receiving house in Avon Street on the outskirts of Stratford, Ontario.

Six weeks later, John Pridmore was standing in line waiting to see if he'd get picked this time. The older, bigger boys were the first to be selected so, with none of them left, he reckoned he was in with a chance. He'd mastered how to milk a cow and to harvest hay, and the hard, physical work was toughening him up. He was worth taking on, even if he did say so himself.

They'd all laughed at how different *this* Stratford was to the one in the East End and some of the group were homesick, but John couldn't see any point in feeling sorry for yourself. He'd been removed from what he'd always thought was a loving family and left in a cold, unfeeling workhouse, then sent on a ship to a far-off country to be placed with strangers. That was life and you just had to make the best of it. His only consolation was that, perhaps, there might be a chance of finding the Batemans – knowing they were already in Canada.

Chester Hammond wasn't too happy to be going all the way to Stratford, but his father was adamant that he shouldn't tarry, as they needed a boy fit for purpose.

'Don't want to be left with only the dregs to choose from,' Patrick Hammond had said, shoving his son out into the early-morning mist. 'Train goes in thirty minutes.'

Notices had appeared all over Grey County announcing the availability of another batch of destitute boys from London, and as this coincided with harvest time Patrick knew there'd be competition for the cheap labour. The notice had also made clear that these children had come from the workhouse and not straight from the streets. Having had a degree of moral teaching and a token education, they'd be snapped up.

Patrick had heard many tales over the years of farmers having trouble with the young ruffians and deviants they called 'street Arabs'. His Irish wife Ellen had begged him not to get one of those. As a Dubliner, she knew that these urchins being cleared from the gutters by do-gooders like Dr Barnardo, himself from Dublin, only knew a life of scavenging and thieving. But there was something more than that troubling Ellen. With her youngest daughter in the throes of puberty, she worried about having a strange lad about the place. She decided that once the apples had been picked, Patrick would have to be persuaded to fill in a reject form and send the ragamuffin on his way.

Chester went up and down the line of boys. He needed an agile specimen, not too heavy – one who'd be able to shin up the apple trees without bruising the fruit. He picked the tallest lad with blond curly hair and a cheeky grin.

'Where are we going?' John asked nervously as the train set off.

'Heading north into Grey County,' answered Chester, opening his newspaper. 'Take us a couple of hours to reach Shallow Lake.' John wanted to ask more questions, but he didn't dare and stared out of the window instead. The scenery passing by was like nothing he could have imagined. Rugged, empty space stretched out for miles, only occasionally broken up by a farm or two. Overcome with a mixture of fear and loneliness, he became very quiet.

'See all the rows of piled-up stones out there?' Chester asked suddenly. 'Boulders were everywhere when the settlers came, they called the place "Stoney Keppel". All had to be cleared before they could plant crops. That was when my pa built our orchard.'

John found Chester's Irish accent comforting – it reminded him of home – and once they got chatting it didn't seem long before they were approaching Shallow Lake. Passing cement works churning out smoke and a noisy sawmill, John thought his new life might not be so different after all.

Patrick Hammond was waiting outside the station exit with the family's buggy. Having secured John's precious box, Chester beckoned to him to squeeze onto the well-worn leather seat. John held on for grim death as the horse started trotting, nearly losing his cap.

'Better get used to that,' Chester said with a laugh, giving his father a sideways glance that said this particular home boy would suit them just fine.

SUNDAY, 24ᵀᴴ DECEMBER 1911

With two days' leave from the *Dunera*, Ernie was spending Christmas with his Aunt Polly and Uncle Jim in Bradley Street. He felt bad about not being with Nance in Cyprus Place, but things were difficult there, what with George's recent accident and Sam being ill. Anyway, Polly had suggested it. Her daughter Mary had been helping in the shop for several months and reported back that Sam was due to go into the union infirmary after Christmas. It was sad, but they couldn't carry on as they were.

Ernie knew about George coming off his delivery bike and breaking his arm badly but struggled to understand quite what was wrong with his uncle. Suffice to say Nance had a lot on her plate, so he'd agreed to the Christmas plan thinking it might also give him time to locate his brothers and sisters.

No one had seen the children in six years. There'd been no hope of bringing them all back together after Bill had died, and time had taken its toll. Ernie knew they'd see him as a stranger. He felt a detachment himself, which was in complete contrast to the connection he had with his Lear cousins.

He loved them all, particularly Daisy, who was bright and breezy and great fun to be around. They often disagreed about things, but Ernie admired her tenacity on the subject of votes for women which never seemed to be far from her lips. He'd even gone to support her on the eve of the new King's Coronation in

June, when she joined forty thousand other women marching for their cause.

Ominously, though, the demonstrations were beginning to turn nasty. In November, the Women's Social & Political Union, feeling betrayed by the Prime Minister, had engaged in mass window smashing. Worried sick, Polly asked Ernie to have a go at talking some sense into her daughter. Not convinced he'd succeed, he nevertheless agreed to meet Daisy coming home from the rubber factory, and while they waited for ages at the White Gates level crossing, he made his plea that she should give up being an activist. She was furious that her one and only ally would ask such a thing, and as soon as the gates opened and the stream of horses and carts piled through, she dragged her cousin into the Duke of Cambridge to give him a piece of her mind. Downing her second port and lemon, she said she knew only too well how much her pay packet was needed to keep the family afloat and wasn't going to risk losing it by breaking the law – but that didn't mean giving up the fight. Suitably chastised, Ernie walked the suffragette home – not daring to catch her eye.

Polly was the one person who knew where all of Ernie's siblings were. Once Sarah had left, she had made it her business to keep a check on them. The workhouse adopted a 'boarding out' policy to reduce the number of children in the school rooms, and Fred had been the first to go. At twelve, not long after his father died, he'd been sent to the Royal Navy training ship *Exmouth*, which was moored just off Grays in Essex. Four years later, he joined HMS *Impregnable* at Devonport, Plymouth. Britain and Germany were in the midst of a naval race to develop the new class of dreadnaught battleships, which meant recruits were needed for a burgeoning navy.

When Joe reached the same age, he had been sent to the National Nautical School for Homeless and Destitute Boys in Portishead, North Somerset. An industrial school, overlooking the Bristol Channel, it had recently opened as a shore-based replacement for the training ship *Formidable*, damaged by severe gales. The institution took in boys under fourteen. Most of the

350 current students had been found begging or wandering the streets, or with parents deemed unfit to look after them. Some came direct from the magistrates' courts.

Polly worried about Joe the most. She'd thought him far too young to be leaving West Ham for such a place and still treasured the only letter he'd sent. Between smudges of ink, he talked of learning shoemaking, carpentry, seamanship and playing in the military band, but his greatest excitement seemed to be sleeping in a hammock in a huge room made to look like the deck of a ship. On the back of the notepaper, he'd sketched the sea-going tender which the school used for practical training. It amused Polly no end to see it was also called *Polly*.

The smell of fried bacon brought Ernie out of his slumber and, realising that the Lear family were already enjoying their leisurely Christmas Eve breakfast, he quickly dressed and squeezed next to Edgar at the table. Polly and her daughters were looking at pictures in the Sunday paper of His Royal Highness King George V and his consort, Queen Mary, during their current visit to India.

'Listen to this,' Polly read out. '*A quarter of a million people were at the Delhi Durbar ceremony to see them proclaimed Emperor and Empress of India. He was wearing the Imperial Crown with eight arches containing six thousand exquisitely cut diamonds and covered with sapphires, emeralds and rubies.* Well I never, can you imagine 'aving to wear that?'

'No, I can't,' Jim sighed, not interested in all the finery. 'Give it 'ere. Does it say anything about HMS *Defence* escorting the Royal Yacht into port? That's all I want to know.'

'Don't think so. Not even a picture. Maybe Fred'll send us a letter or a postcard if he gets the chance. Wonder what 'e's doing right now?'

'Scrubbing the decks, I daresay. Reckon the King'll be able to eat 'is dinner off 'em when 'e gets back from this. It says, *King George, an avid hunter, is going on a ten-day big game hunt in Nepal.* Can't see Fred riding on the back of elephants, shooting tigers,' Jim chortled.

Before entering commercial service, the P&O liner *Medina* had been requisitioned for use as a royal yacht for the state visit to India. Sailing from Portsmouth on 11th November, armoured cruisers *Argyll*, *Cochrane*, *Natal* and *Defence* were her escorts. Ordinary seaman Frederick Pridmore was serving on HMS *Defence*.

'This is what your brother's up to,' Jim said to his nephew, handing over some of the newspaper. Ernie, his mouth already full of greasy bacon and fried bread, looked and nodded in agreement.

'Reckon Joe'll be overseas too soon,' Polly added. ''E'll be transferring to the Navy in Chatham when 'e's sixteen. That just leaves 'arry. I'm so glad you went to see 'im last night, Ernie.'

'Just 'ave to 'ope 'e comes for a visit now you've asked 'im,' said Daisy, prodding Ernie in the ribs as she gathered the washing-up.

'Can't force 'im, though, can we, love?' said Jim, putting a comforting arm around his daughter. 'But at least 'e's only in Stratford.'

Daisy had often wondered what the long-term consequences would be of her cousins being sent to the workhouse. Harry seemed to have felt the severing of family ties the most. He'd been boarded out as a builder's apprentice when he was fourteen and had kept himself to himself ever since. The shame was never far from the surface, so Harry's reluctance to keep in touch wasn't discussed at home. Daisy knew exactly how Ernie felt about it, though.

'You should visit the girls before Lily goes into service. Be 'arder afterwards,' Polly said to him somewhat desperately. 'Why don't you go this afternoon, take 'em a little something for Christmas?'

Lily, Betsy and Ada had remained the responsibility of the West Ham Guardians but were no longer living in the workhouse. The union had started renting houses in Leytonstone, Forest Gate, Wanstead and Woodford operating a scattered home system where up to twelve girls or boys lived in a single house under the care and supervision of a house parent. They attended local schools too. Whilst this was an infinitely better way to bring up the poor law children, Polly was saddened to think of all three girls being in different places.

Ernie popped to the sweet shop, bought three boxes of sugared almonds wrapped in seasonal paper and made his way to Forest Gate. By midday he had already spent an all-too-brief time with one of his sisters.

Bitterly cold, by the time he got to his second stop at 36 Pulteney Road, Woodford, it was starting to sleet. A young girl showed him into her house mother's private room, where he didn't dare sit down in his wet overcoat and so stood uncomfortably by the unlit fire. The encounter with timid Betsy had not been a great success and he feared that Ada, being even younger, might react in the same way. Ernie knew it was going to take time to gain their trust. Both girls were babies when they were institutionalised, so there was no chance they'd remember him or anyone else in the family he might mention.

When the door finally opened, a wary nine-year-old was pushed in. The door closed again, leaving the two of them alone. Trying a different tack to Betsy, Ernie did his best to make Ada feel at ease by pretending to lose the sweets and then producing each one from behind her ear. It worked: she laughed hysterically. With the ice broken, the promise of regular visits went down well.

Luckily, the meeting with Lily at Leytonstone was not hard work at all. She remembered both her older brothers and was shocked to hear of Bill's tragic drowning. Ernie recalled her tomboy nature and, despite being only months away from starting work, Lily looked like she'd just climbed down the tree they used to sit in in St Luke's Square. Her hair pins were struggling to do their job and her apron was already grubby, but the most striking thing was that she looked just like their mother.

The tram was nearly empty by the time Ernie travelled back to Canning Town. He was looking forward to returning to Polly and Jim's warm kitchen and to sharing in a family Christmas. What saddened him was that none of his siblings knew what a proper home life was. It made him realise how truly grateful he was that he hadn't gone into the workhouse with them. He owed it to his aunts to make the most of himself, move up in the world and make them proud.

WEDNESDAY, 10TH APRIL 1912

Ernie's job interview with the steam tug and towing operation at Southampton dock had lasted longer than he'd anticipated, and he'd been itching to join the huge crowd on the quayside to watch the RMS *Titanic* setting off on her maiden voyage.

There were other great ships in the dock – like the *Majestic*, at ten thousand tons moored just a few cables away – which made for an impressive sight, but they were dwarfed by the colossal *Titanic*. At forty-six thousand tons, nine hundred feet long and one hundred feet high, Ernie could only marvel at her towering decks and the power that her gleaming propellers would generate.

Liners like the *Majestic*, *St Louis* and the *Philadelphia* had been breaking records on trans-Atlantic crossings, but *Titanic* was already being heralded as the world's fastest ship. In the brilliant spring sunshine, as the vast steel wall began to move, no one in the cheering crowd would have doubted such a claim.

Slowly and silently the White Star liner glided away from her berth – Ernie paying particular notice to the six steam tugs *Albert*, *Edward*, *Hercules*, *Vulcan*, *Ajax*, *Hector* and *Neptune* in place to offer assistance. Suddenly a sound like a revolver firing made him look towards the *New York* – another liner berthed at the same quay but laid up owing to the ongoing coal strike. On entering the open stream of Southampton Water, the gigantic *Titanic* had sucked the water between her and the quay to such a degree that the strain broke the three-inch steel hawsers securing the *New York*.

There were gasps from the crowd as the smaller vessel began drifting stern-first towards the outgoing liner, broken cables hanging down her side. People rushed to get a better view, some climbing onto railway trucks to witness the expected collision, but Ernie's eyes remained fixed on the tugs. As *Titanic* reversed her engines, the *Neptune* and *Vulcan* raced towards the *New York*, catching her with ropes by the bows, turning her back to the quay. Ernie scratched his head in amazement. With the collision averted, the giant propellers of the *Titanic* started to turn again, churning the green sea into liquid grey mud as she glided safely away out to sea. The two thousand or so passengers and crew aboard were so full of high spirits, they barely noticed the delay.

On the train journey home, Ernie mulled over whether he should take the job on offer in Southampton dock. There was no doubt that working on one of the tugs he'd just watched ply their trade so deftly would be a rewarding challenge, but with wages falling and the cost of living increasing, the whole country was gripped by a wave of strikes. Tug companies went out of business at the best of times, so leaving one for another at this time could be a very risky move.

The unrest had started with the Welsh miners and was soon followed by cotton workers and boilermakers. At the beginning of 1911 seamen walked out, and in August, as the country sweltered in a heatwave, discontent spread to London's docks. The smell of rotting fish and meat made Ernie wretch. Barrels of rancid butter and piles of rotting vegetables lay everywhere. The Government brought in armed police and the military to try to break the men, which resulted in soldiers shooting dead two dockers. Within days, six further deaths occurred when railway workers began their first-ever national strike. Faced with an outright challenge to their authority, the Government compromised and granted concessions to the dockers and railwaymen, but the conflict continued.

Not long after Christmas, with poverty fuelling the growing militancy, a million coal miners came out in support of a minimum wage. Consequently, more and more ships were moored up in the docks due to lack of fuel. When a rumour circulated that the Transport Workers Federation were threatening a general strike involving docks nationwide, Ernie feared the worst for everyone's jobs.

THURSDAY, 25TH APRIL 1912

Henry Cook Pridmore stood in the churchyard of St Luke's feeling every bit his sixty-seven years. He'd been gone from Canning Town for the last eight, after relocating his marine business to Wisbech, and time seemed to be passing with alarming speed. The open fenland, fresh air and Maud's home cooking suited him well, but today, his head was flooding with old memories. He felt the weight of his family's problems on his shoulders again.

Sam's funeral was still in progress, but his father had needed to come out of the church early to compose himself. It was extremely painful accepting that both his sons were now dead at barely half his age. The truth about their illness was hard to swallow and Henry totally understood why no one had wanted to talk about it. He also knew he owed Nance an incredible debt of gratitude for ensuring that Sam hadn't suffered the same terrible end as had Joseph.

Nance had watched his symptoms mimic his brother's for over a year. She'd brushed aside grandiose plans and made light of unpredictable behaviour. Once the tremors and stutters started, she kept her husband out of the shop and away from prying eyes, nursing him at home until she could manage it no more. It came as a great relief when he was admitted to the union infirmary for the few weeks before the paralytic coma finally ended his life.

Sam suspected what fate had in store for him the minute he was given his brother's death certificate at the asylum. He knew that death from untreated syphilis in its final stage was termed General Paralysis of the Insane and, in all likelihood, he had it too.

Like many young men who couldn't wait until they were married, Sam had followed in Joseph's footsteps visiting the notorious slum north of Woolwich High Street. With coal wharves lining the riverside creating an atmosphere heavy with thick dust, the area between Beresford Street and Warren Lane was known as the 'Dusthole'. At the end of the nineteenth century, prostitution prevailed and many of the houses were brothels. So worried were the Army about the spread of the pox that they placed sentries at the entrances to prevent soldiers from the Arsenal who might be tempted to stray inside. After negotiating a price to sow his first wild oats, Sam soon developed irritation, then sores, patchy rashes and a fever. It was enough to put him off making another visit, but after a month or two the symptoms disappeared and, thinking he'd recovered, forgot all about it.

When the church doors opened, Henry was delighted to see his eldest grandson supporting Nance and her son George – his arm in a splint – down the steps. Ernie was no longer the scrawny, pale and underfed kiddie he remembered so well. Coming towards Henry now was a strong, healthy man with striking blue eyes and thick, dark hair. He had all the Irish good looks of his mother and aunts.

'You still got that rusty armour and old swords?' Ernie asked, smiling broadly as they shook hands. 'Coming across to the Charrington?'

Henry had every intention of joining the mourners, but there was someone he needed to talk to first.

'Set one up for me, son,' he replied with a wink. 'I'll be there in a little while.'

Eliza, shunned by Nance and Polly, had been sitting at the back during the service. Everyone was well aware of her presence as her three squirming, screaming children had disrupted the proceedings more than once. With the first taste of spring, they were now running around the gravestones completely out of control. Henry moved towards his unkempt daughter, trying to hide his disappointment. He'd been sending her money again of late, but it wasn't hard to see that much of it had gone on gin. With a threadbare skirt and dirty hair, Henry was relieved his wife wasn't with him. Maud had been disgusted at Eliza's behaviour ever since she'd found out what had happened to little Grace Alice four years ago. It had been a bone of contention ever since.

During one of their many rows, Eliza had blurted out to Harold Pike that the eldest child he was providing for wasn't actually his. Feeling a sap for falling for her lies at the time, and now struggling to feed two more babies, he made her take Grace to the workhouse to join her other fatherless siblings, Rachel and John. The child was just three and a bright little thing. Maud had sleepless nights picturing her pretty face as she was handed over.

Henry understood why the women in the family felt little compassion for Eliza, but no one could blame her for what happened next. In January 1910, Harold had left for work as usual. He hadn't gone far when he collapsed in the street, sending the tins of paint he was carrying rolling in the gutter. He'd suffered a fatal heart attack aged just thirty-nine, leaving Eliza seven months pregnant.

Putting his arms around his daughter's thin body, Henry held her tight. He could feel her ribs pressing against his own ample chest as she sobbed on his shoulder.

'First Joseph, then 'arold, now Sam,' she whispered. 'I've got no one to turn to no more. You won't desert me, will you, Pa?'

'I'll do my best,' he nodded, 'but Maud wants me to give up the marine stores and retire, so money'll be a bit short then. But right now, let's go down Rathbone Street and get you some food from teapot Jones. 'If I've got any coppers left,' he winked, 'I'll get the little'uns some penny toys from the pedlar.'

Eliza smiled and pulled away to retrieve her brood, now causing havoc in the street.

A large glass of whisky was waiting on the bar when Henry got back to the Charrington Arms. He downed it quickly and bought another round for Nance, George, Ernie, Polly and Jim sitting at a table in the corner. They'd been through some hard times and it told on all their pale faces. There was a quiet discussion going on about the future of the shop, which George, now fifteen, was adamant he was more than capable of taking over. Well aware of Nance's strength and fortitude, Henry was in no doubt that it would be her name above the door from now on. With a wife cut from the same cloth, Jim knew it too and the men exchanged knowing glances.

At the end of the evening, Ernie offered to walk his grandfather back to the Clarendon Hotel where his bed awaited him.

'So I hear you're going to work for this new Port of London Authority. Better security, I imagine.'

'Well, it should be, but I 'ave to start off on an 'opper dredging the Thames,' sniffed Ernie. 'It's so they can build the new King George V dock. Reckon it's gunna take nine years, so just 'ave to 'ope I'm not there till the bitter end.'

After much deliberation, Able Seaman Ernest Joseph Pridmore had made the decision to leave the United Steam Tug Company for the newly created Port of London Authority, which was still feeling its feet. Its brief was to bring order to the chaos and congestion that prevailed on the Thames, assuming responsibility for the enclosed docks, the conservation of the river for seventy miles and for the registration of watermen, lightermen and their craft.

From Ernie's point of view the PLA offered hope of a job with better long-term prospects and a weekly wage of one pound and twelve shillings.

'And I also heard you're playing football for a team down there in Kent,' Henry said as they reached Hoy Street.

'That's right.' Ernie smiled, guessing where this conversation was going. 'Gravesend 'otspurs.'

'Can't believe you've deserted our beloved West Ham after

all the times we went to watch them together,' sniffed Henry, feigning annoyance. 'Not to mention the other matches you climbed over the fence with Bill to see.'

Stopping on the footbridge over the Stratford to North Woolwich railway, the pair exchanged memories of that brief but happy time over a cigarette or two. It was a nice ending to a difficult day. The road traffic leaving Victoria Dock was piling up by the level crossing just as it always had. Looking across to the Thames Ironworks' wall opposite Henry said it was a change not to see the huge bulk of a ship under construction looming above it. Ernie nodded without saying anything. He knew that the battleship HMS *Thunderer*, launched only last year, was likely to be the river Thames' final contribution to the Royal Navy.

During its fifty-year lifetime, navies from all around the world had placed orders with the yard. But, these days, it was shipyards in the north that claimed most of the Admiralty's budget. Ironwork's owner, Arnold Hills, had even petitioned Winston Churchill over the lack of orders, but his plea fell on deaf ears. Once the banks got wind of the situation, they withdrew their loans and the yard had been empty ever since. It was another disaster for the local community. Out-of-work metal workers swelled the number of unemployed men already hanging around the streets and all this at a time when Britain was experiencing its greatest ever naval shipbuilding boom.

Henry sighed. Canning Town had been dealt one blow after another. He wondered what the current generation made of it all. Thinking back to when he'd first lived in Stephenson Street, having to wade through stagnant river water and filth, perhaps today wasn't so bad.

Later, as he drifted off to sleep, he thought about all he'd learned during the day. Eliza was a constant worry and heaven knows what would become of her brood, but at least it was a relief to hear that his other grandchildren were finding their feet – one in the PLA, and two now serving on His Majesty's warships. Then there was Polly and Nance, who had done their best for the family despite years of hard toil and hadn't changed one dot.

WEDNESDAY, 24TH JUNE 1914

Daisy looked in the mirror. Fortunately, her eye was no longer swollen and the bruising could just about be disguised by a liberal coating of face powder. Hopefully it was enough to stop her mother going on about it yet again.

Marching in a suffragette procession had become a risky business. She had taken to carrying a 'Saturday nights' – a length of hemp rope, knotted at one end – which, hidden in her sleeve, could be used as a cosh if necessary. She only wished she'd done it sooner. Apart from the pain and humiliation, coming home with a black eye had caused one almighty row.

Sylvia Pankhurst, daughter of Emmeline, had recently started the East London Federation of Suffragettes, with a branch in West Ham. Daisy still shied away from their more militant activities, but she regularly attended the meetings on Beckton Corner and distributed the group's newspaper, the *Woman's Dreadnaught*, around the Tidal Basin. When an appeal went out for all suffragettes to attend a march on 21st May, Daisy thought it her duty to join in.

With the aim of petitioning the King at Buckingham Palace, the women made their way through Admiralty Arch to the Victoria Memorial. Surprised to see a large crowd of people already there and with their backs to the memorial, Daisy noticed that most of them were youths. There was a wide-open space between the people and the palace, in the middle of which was a line of police.

Waving their banners and proclaiming their cause, every now and then a suffragette would dart out from amongst the spectators into the space. When caught by a policeman, she was then thrown back into the crowd. Daisy was horrified. Once in the hands of angry young men, they would beat her, tear her clothes and pull her hair down. Astonishingly, the suffragettes ran out again and again, only to receive the same treatment. The police never attempted to arrest anyone or to protect those who were assaulted, even when one young woman was lifted right up and thrown over the heads of the nearest people. Eventually, mounted police came up at a gallop and drove everyone away. Separated from her colleagues, Daisy was swept down Birdcage Walk. Aware that some jeering lads were behind her, she stopped and faced them. A boy, several years younger than her brother Edgar, stepped forward, striking her in the face with his fist. 'You deserved that,' he sneered as they ran off.

Sylvia Pankhurst had already been arrested and sentenced nine times since the beginning of the year and had gone on hunger strike to underline her protest. Tired of the sympathy she and others were receiving, the authorities were trying a new tack. There was no shortage of young men, fuelled by the prospect of war, to do their silent bidding.

Going home to a new husband in such a state simply confirmed Bill Turrell's worst fears. He'd worried about Daisy's involvement with the suffragettes ever since she'd gone to Emily Davison's funeral when they were first courting. To him it seemed unbelievable that women would resort to property destruction, arson and bombings. Why anyone would deliberately undertake acts of violence to get a prison sentence and then go on hunger strike only to be force fed, was beyond him. But to die for the cause, like Emily had done by throwing herself in front of the King's horse at the Epsom Derby, seemed insane.

As Bill smeared Zam-Buk on his wife's bruised face, he kept quiet. She was upset enough. Besides, he knew her mother would have plenty to say for all of them.

Satisfied with her make-up and carrying the latest *Dreadnaught* under her arm, Daisy and Bill Turrell set off for their tea at Bradley Street. Saturday, the 20th June had turned out to be a significant day for the working-class women of the East End, and Daisy was keen to tell her mother and sisters about it.

Six members of the ELFS had been granted an audience with Prime Minister Asquith. Led by Julia Scurr of Limehouse, they were: Mrs Hughes, a brushmaker; Mrs Bird, mother of six young children; Mrs Ford, a widow with three children; Mrs Payne, a shoemaker from Bow and Daisy Parsons, representing West Ham.

Daisy Lear had been at Beckton Road School with Daisy Parsons and Polly knew her mother. With a sickly husband, she had kept the family together by charring while her daughter looked after her five younger brothers. At twelve, Daisy Parsons had gone to work at a cigarette factory, which was when the girls had lost touch.

The *Dreadnaught*'s account of the successful meeting went down well with Polly. She studied it in great detail and read aloud Daisy Parsons' speech and Asquith's reply while everyone tucked into their shrimp and watercress sandwiches. Her own daughter's fading black eye hardly got a mention.

'As a young mother I have three little girls to bring up, two of my own children and another, a little niece who has neither father nor mother. I feel if we women are able to perform the high duty of motherhood – and after all there are mothers who have brought statesmen into the world, because they have all had mothers, and we bring sailors, policemen and everybody into the world – we should at least have a say as to how those children should be brought up. When I had the first little girl, I had a conscientious objection to vaccination and I went to the local magistrates for an exemption order. I thought I would save time by filling the form in and I presented it to him. The magistrate laughed and said you cannot do

anything with this, you are not the parent. But, I said, I am the mother, surely I know what is good for my own child. But he said that in the eyes of the law you are not the parent of your own child. We feel that it is an insult to us. When we bring children into the world we should at least be able to say what is good for them. We mothers are with the children more than the fathers are, and in the event of a dock strike, or any other strike for that matter, it is the mother who has to do the ferreting and has the work to do and perform her household duties as well.'

Asquith gave a conciliatory reply to the deputation and indicated to them that their delegation was more representative than others he had met. He declared, 'If the change [women's suffrage] has got to come we must face it boldly and make it thoroughly democratic in its basis.' It appeared that Asquith had finally recognised that he could not maintain his resistance to women's suffrage much longer.

TUESDAY, 15ᵀᴴ SEPTEMBER 1914

Polly shivered every time she saw the recruitment poster. His index finger pointing directly at her, with the words *Your Country Needs You*, was unsettling. Even Nance had a poster in her shop window. It was Field-Marshal Lord Kitchener's rallying cry to the young men of the nation to support King and Country by joining the Army. Since August 4th, the day Britain declared war on Germany, nearly half a million had joined up – London's working class proving to be enthusiastic volunteers. With two fit sons of recruitment age, Polly was worried. Nance was alright, though. She knew her son was safe. George's withered arm wouldn't pass the medical. It looked like his bicycle accident might turn out to be a blessing in disguise.

The newspapers were reporting a quarter of a million French casualties in the first month alone. Soldiers of the British Expeditionary Force, fighting alongside their French counterparts, were unable to penetrate German defences and had already sustained heavy casualties during hostilities along the Aisne River. With neither side able to advance, the situation had reached a stalemate. Trenches were being dug and preparations made for a war of attrition on what was coming to be known as 'The Western Front' – running all the way from the North Sea, through Belgium and France, to the Swiss border.

Getting men to enlist wasn't a problem at the beginning of the war. As long as you were unmarried and between eighteen and forty-one, you could volunteer. Conscription wasn't deemed necessary at this stage. There was a distinct air of optimism about holding Fritz to account and the papers were full of how *it would all be over by Christmas*. Many men joined up to escape arduous and humdrum jobs, and locally raised Pals battalions promised men from the same community or workplace the chance of fighting together.

More than 14,500 men from West Ham volunteered to serve in the various units, including their Member of Parliament. Five volunteer battalions were formed in East and West Ham with four additional gun brigades raised by Thames Ironworks, and one of the Pals battalions, the 13th/Essex Regiment, shouted their football team's chant 'Up the Irons!' as they advanced into battle.

Polly watched the mothers drying their eyes on their aprons as their sons marched along the Barking Road silently praying that she wouldn't soon be doing the same. Her William was courting and had a good job. It was Edgar she thought more likely to be swept along to 'do his bit'.

'At least I don't 'ave to worry about Daisy no more,' she reminded her husband as the boys disappeared into the distance.

The queue at the Canning Town distribution centre stretched down the street and round the corner long before it opened. The ELFS still campaigned for the vote and held frequent meetings, but much of their work was done relieving the distress caused by the war. They had decided to give one pint of milk to mothers and children each day. In order to raise money for the fund, Daisy Parsons took her daughter to Oxford Street and begged in order to raise the five pounds necessary. She'd also been co-opted onto the Distress Committee of West Ham Borough Council and visited those who were in distress.

Daisy Turrell had been giving out milk and eggs for hours and still had an afternoon's washing-up at the Women's Hall in Bow to look forward to. She counted her blessings that her own family was being spared the hardship others were having in finding a few pennies each day to pay for a hot meal of meat pudding, potatoes, greens and a slice of spotted dick.

Almost as soon as the war had broken out, factories across East London had closed and food prices spiralled, pushing many to the brink of starvation. Sugar, which used to cost one and a half pence a pound was now three times more. Local women, struggling to pay their rent with their husbands away or killed in action, began calling at the cost-price canteen run by the East London Federation of Suffragettes. Feeling she needed to help, Daisy was volunteering there. Bill Turrell wasn't best pleased that his new wife was away from home so much. She was working punishing hours, but he was proud of her for doing it. Besides, the women running these relief projects were neighbours to those they were helping.

SATURDAY, 12TH DECEMBER 1914

The war was changing everything – leastways that's how Bill saw it. The suffragettes didn't have time for violence anymore; besides, there was enough of that going on in Belgium. Since mid-October, British casualties during the fighting in the Ypres salient exceeded fifty thousand and as reports of enemy atrocities against the civilian population in the country began to circulate, people started to turn on German-sounding members of their own communities.

The East End of London had always had a large German population originally working in the poorly paid and physically demanding job of sugar boiling. Their influence, in trades like chemical-processing and glass-manufacturing, was felt too, but these days they ran small businesses, such as barbers, bakers and butchers, and some were school masters and governesses. A German band playing in the street was a familiar sight and much enjoyed. Nothing could have prepared them for the level of hostility they were beginning to face as public opinion turned against them and internment was introduced.

At dawn on the 6th November, Carl Hans Lody was the first of eleven German spies to be shot in the Tower of London. It had been 150 years since the last person was executed there and it didn't go down well when their bodies were brought all the way to Plaistow cemetery for burial – especially when news broke that they were to get a tombstone. Most East End families couldn't afford such a memorial for their own loved ones. And when it was reported that a German internment camp was soon to open in Carpenters Road, Stratford, Bill Turrell echoed the feelings of many: 'It's always the East End that gets the rubbish.'

'Can you get Daisy to put in a good word for me?' Eliza Pridmore pleaded with Polly Lear as she sat in her kitchen. 'I really need a job, especially one that'll look after 'arold Junior while I'm working.'

Jim was trying to keep an eye on her son as he rifled through the drawers of their dresser. Neither he nor his wife looked too pleased about it all.

'Well, I'll ask 'er,' Polly replied, wagging her finger at the unruly child, 'but I doubt she 'as much say in who gets taken on.'

Sensing she'd outstayed her welcome, Eliza stood up. 'That's all I'm asking, Poll. I ain't got no money, so Lord knows what future my children 'ave got.' She grabbed hold of Harold Junior to stop him pulling faces at Alf, who was getting restless and making a noise.

'At least Rachel and Grace, my two eldest girls, will 'ave a better life now,' she declared on reaching the back door. 'They're in Ontario, Canada, just like their brother John. Been there since the end of March. Rachel's already got a job as a domestic. Grace will too, soon as she's old enough.'

Polly, clearly taken aback by what she'd just heard, raised her eyes at her husband. She thought it inconceivable that any mother could be happy about having three children on the other side of the world.

'They got moved from the workhouse into Dr Barnardo's,' Eliza continued blithely.

''E took over two 'undred girls to Canada – on the *Sicilian*. Won't be no more going till the war's over now, though.'

Polly silently wondered if that meant the other three children would eventually be following in their footsteps.

'I can't, Ma,' Daisy said later, looking perplexed. 'I 'ave no say in who gets a job in the toy factory. Besides, they're nearly all women whose 'usbands 'ave died in the trenches.'

'I know, and I told 'er exactly that,' Polly replied with a sigh. 'Truth is she's a law unto 'erself.'

Local builders and tradesmen had helped Sylvia Pankhurst fit out a small factory in Norman Grove, Bow. Realising that toys were no longer being imported from Germany, she'd hit upon the idea of getting women to design and make stuffed dolls, animals, wooden houses and trains. They received a living wage of one pound a week with a crèche provided for their young children. The toys were so well made that Sylvia filled a taxi with them and headed off to Oxford Street, where Gordon Selfridge needed little persuasion to stock them in his Oxford Street store.

Polly was still cross over Eliza Pridmore's visit when she was washing up the tea things later. Compared to Daisy Parsons, who fought to be acknowledged as the parent of her children and to have a say in their welfare, Eliza seemed only too happy to hand that responsibility over to someone else. It seemed unnatural, almost callous. The more Polly thought about it, the more she realised Eliza's actions were all too reminiscent of those carried out by her own sister Sarah. She'd abandoned her little ones too. It had been nearly ten years and not once had she been back.

No wonder she felt angry.

While Ernie had been celebrating the completion of his apprenticeship on his twenty-third birthday, the PLA were busy re-deploying their workers in readiness for war. Transferred to Tilbury Dock pier-head, he was now lockman for a dock that was at full stretch with many more ships lying in the river waiting for berths.

Coming off duty and waiting on the quayside for the steam ferry to take him across to Gravesend, his body ached for sleep. Everyone felt the same and no one was talking. A blast from the *Catherine*'s horn signalled she was on her way and Ernie fastened his donkey jacket in readiness for the chilly, one-mile journey across the river.

As they were climbing aboard, the train station door flew open and a large group of elderly civilians were marched out by an armed guard. Ernie realised they were German and had to be heading for the *Batavier V*, a Dutch ship currently moored at Gravesend, bound for Rotterdam. It took some time to get them all on board and even longer to get their luggage stowed. Resigned to having to stay awake somewhat longer than expected, Ernie watched the commotion with amusement.

As soon as the *Catherine* came alongside Gravesend's Town Pier, Dutch sailors started transferring suitcases and boxes. One particularly heavy wooden box, fastened with a padlock and with the words non-poisonous on the side, couldn't be pushed or dragged. After much debate, the sweating men resorted to rolling it over and over. They had just got to the gangway when, to their astonishment, the lid gave way and an arm appeared. 'Man inside!' someone shouted, and in seconds the stowaway was being dragged out by two armed guards from the *Batavier*. He was a young man about six feet tall, with a fair moustache and dressed in a lounge suit – and from what Ernie could see, must have been a contortionist to fit inside the crate. Unsurprisingly, he struggled to stand having been doubled up for nearly fifteen hours. Investigation of the box's other contents revealed two champagne bottles filled with water, a bottle of meat extract, bananas and a pillow filled with oxygen.

It turned out the man was a German Army officer, Lieutenant Otto Koehn, on his way home from America when war was declared. He'd been arrested in Southampton and sent to a Prisoner of War and Internment camp in Dorchester, Dorset. Hearing that a group of German civilians in the camp were being released from detention and repatriated, he'd seen a chance to resume his own journey. As a soldier he knew they wouldn't release him while the war was on, so any means of escape had to be tried.

Koehn got no further than Gravesend Police Station before being sent back to Dorchester. Ernie watched him as he was being escorted away. It seemed odd to think that only a few months earlier this young man would have been just another passenger in transit on the way home. Now he was the enemy.

FRIDAY, 25ᵀᴴ DECEMBER 1914

Christmas had come and the war hadn't ended, nor did it look like it was going to end anytime soon. In just five months the British had already lost thirty-seven thousand men.

Ernie stood looking at the pontoon bridge recently built across the Thames to speed up troop movements. Stretching 850 yards from the Clarendon Hotel on the Kent side to the World's End public house in Essex, its centre section had to be moored along the riverbank during the day to allow vessels through. It took two hours to tow out and another two to tow back and was driving the skippers barmy having to 'stand by' all day with steam up in case of alarm.

Not today, Ernie said to himself, his words disappearing on the wind. With St George's Church bells chiming behind him, he turned and started on the short walk to 6 Bernard Street and the Christmas dinner he was about to share with his girl and her family.

Ada opened the door, but before she and Ernie could exchange a word, her two young sisters had wormed their way in front in a fit of giggles. It was the first time Hilda, aged nine, and Mabel, two years her junior, had seen Ada's beau, and they were silly with excitement. Shooing them away, Ada pulled Ernie inside and as he hung his jacket on the hallstand, he dared to give her a quick peck on the cheek. A loud cough from the parlour signalled that they should enter and on opening the door a cloud of pipe smoke engulfed them.

Bill Stone, in his Sunday best for Christmas Day, smoothed down his moustache with one bandaged hand and shook Ernie's hand gingerly by the other. Thankfully they weren't strangers. Bill's badly chafed and cracked skin was the tell-tale sign of someone who'd been heaving sacks of West Indies sugar for many a year. Their paths had often crossed at Tilbury. In fact, it was when Ada had brought her sisters down to the ferry to meet their father that Ernie had first spotted her, and rather liked what he saw.

Not long after, on a glorious Sunday afternoon, Ernie left his lodgings in Berkley Road and strolled through the Fort Gardens towards the riverfront. The promenade was busy with families enjoying the sunshine. Mothers with prams watched their children playing games on the grass, while husbands took others to paddle in the murky water. Seeing Ada walking alone, he did his best to catch her eye by removing his straw boater and smiling broadly as he passed. Doubling back, a few yards further on, he did the same. On the third attempt it worked – Ada laughed uncontrollably. They'd been walking out for two months now and Christmas Day seemed the perfect opportunity for family introductions.

Mrs Stone, another Ada, took off her pinnie to welcome Ernie into the steamy kitchen, but soon had it on again to serve up the turkey, spuds and greens. As they exchanged pleasantries, Ernie realised her accent was much like his and after establishing that she came from Poplar, banter about street names and places quickly broke the ice.

With the plum pudding boiling so furiously that Ada had to get a bucket to catch the dripping condensation, everyone squeezed around the table. Bill said a prayer for his wife's nephew and all the other boys on the Western Front who had nothing more to look forward to than bully beef for their Christmas dinner.

Ernie skirted around being asked about his own parents and instead talked warmly about his family in Canning Town and how his Aunt Nance had brought him up in the shop in Cyprus

Place. Explaining that she'd taught him to read and write and to play a few chords on the piano spurred Hilda and Mabel to beg Ernie to have a go on their upright as soon as they'd left the table. 'It's a Long Way to Tipperary', which he'd learned by ear, brought a tear to everyone's eye and a particularly comical rendition of 'When Father Papered the Parlour' had the girls shrieking for more. Although pretending she wasn't amused by his tomfoolery, Ada loved every minute of it and before the end of the evening, another visit had been planned.

Ada Sophia Stone had had a very different childhood to Ernie. She was born in Gravesend to loving parents and spent her first twelve years as an only child until Hilda came along. Not that she'd been without company. Her mother's sister had several children and, living close by in Clarendon Road, Ada often helped look after them. Hearing how barefoot Ernie had dragged his younger brothers around the East End streets in all weathers broke her heart. Her father was by no means well off, but with only one child to support, she'd had nice clothes and a good education. Good enough that on leaving school she'd been able to get a job as a grocery assistant in David Grieg's.

Ernie might play the court jester, constantly teasing, pulling out hair pins and prancing around in one of her hats, but it was clear he would do anything for her. Determined to make something of himself and be able to provide for a family, Ada was becoming ever fonder of him. She especially loved the way his blue eyes sparkled when he looked at her.

As dawn broke on the Western Front that frosty Christmas Day, Ada's cousin Jack, on lookout in the forward trenches, was amazed to see unarmed German soldiers climbing over their parapets and wandering across No Man's Land towards him shouting in English 'not to fire!' One of the British officers went out to meet them and, after what looked to be a friendly conversation, an unofficial truce was declared. Soon soldiers on both sides were climbing out of their trenches and fraternising until the battlefield was a sea of grey and khaki. Souvenirs were swapped, and bully beef and Tickler's jam bartered for barrels of French beer. Men who only hours before had been firing at each other now posed together in groups for photographs, and when a keen sportsman from the Bedfordshire Regiment produced a football, scratch teams of up to fifty a side played enthusiastically until the ball finally gave up the ghost. Bands played and singing could be heard across the front. For a brief moment the war was forgotten. It was to be the last time for four long years.

SATURDAY, 15TH MAY 1915

Ernie and Ada had set off early for the train from Gravesend to London Bridge. It was her turn to meet his family, so thinking that they'd start with the streets he'd grown up in, they alighted at Custom House. Ernie quickly realised it wasn't a good idea as the rioting near Victoria dock had obviously been particularly bad. Broken glass was everywhere as every second butcher's or baker's shop in the maze of little streets was German. Childhood memories of the mouth-watering smell of fresh bread and spicy currant buns flooded back. Then he'd always been hungry and never noticed the names above the doors. Now he felt irresponsible for bringing Ada here, especially after their experiences in Gravesend only a few days earlier.

On that springtime evening, Ada had chivvied 'Are we going? It'll be dark before we get this walk.' As they strolled along Bernard Street, she tucked her arm through his, acknowledging the looming grey clouds.

'Doesn't look like we should go up Windmill Hill,' Ernie said. 'Better stay nearby.'

They hadn't gone far when a large and rowdy crowd of men, women and children surged past them heading for the High Street. Holding on to Ada tightly, Ernie doubled back towards the river to see what was going on. A ferry load of angry dockers were coming up from the Town Pier. Suddenly there was a sound of smashing glass which confirmed Ernie's worst fears.

Seeing Ada home for her own safety, he made his way back to the High Street to witness Glassons furniture store with its windows all broken and the contents either stolen or smashed to pieces – even heavy mangles and bedsteads. The three hundred-strong mob was marching off along New Road looking for other targets on which to vent their aggression. The Half-Penny Bazaar narrowly escaped the same treatment after someone shouted out, 'Russian Jew, leave it.' But Thomas Schultz, a local stationer and printer, wasn't so lucky. Although born in Stepney and living in Gravesend for more than fifty years, he had a German name and that was enough for missiles to be thrown.

It was eight o'clock and beginning to rain. Ernie stood back in the shadow of a doorway and lit a cigarette as a group of police officers arrived. But their presence did nothing to stop the gang surging forward into the shop, looting or damaging its contents beyond repair. They continued down King Street until they were met by armed soldiers with fixed bayonets coming from the barracks.

'It's for the Lusitania,' Bill Stone had explained later as Ernie dried out with a mug of tea in his hands. 'Germans showed no mercy with her, so it's not surprising people are taking it out on the ones living on our own doorstep.'

On the 7th May, Cunard's Blue Riband passenger liner RMS *Lusitania* had been torpedoed by a German submarine off the coast of Ireland, with the loss of 1,198 lives, including women and children. Serious anti-German rioting began in Liverpool, the home port of the *Lusitania*, but soon spread like wildfire to the rest of the country. London got it the worst, with six days of frenzied attacks on nearly two thousand premises, most in the East End.

Now back in the East End, they were having to wind their way carefully through the mess. Every establishment had been ransacked, with doors hanging off their hinges. Some were completely empty inside, their occupants nowhere to be seen. Ada was shocked to see that the frenzied violence had extended to homes as well as shops. Cupboards, furniture and even staircases had been hacked to pieces.

'Looks like their belongings have been carted off by the barrow load,' she said, daring to look inside. 'It's a miracle no one's been killed.'

'More than 'undred coppers got injured, though,' Ernie replied. 'Stuck in the middle.'

'So you've seen Canning Town in all its glory,' said Daisy on her doorstep. 'Poplar came in for it too. Some Germans got thrown out of their 'ouses onto the street. Terrible, ain't it?'

Ada raised her eyes to the ceiling as she gratefully took the cup of tea on offer.

'Don't get me wrong,' said Polly, taking up the baton as she passed the *Daily Sketch* to Ernie. On the front page was a picture of a huge crowd watching a piano being lowered out of an upstairs window. 'I don't want them Germans 'ere no more, but I don't think they should 'ave 'ad all their stuff nicked. Old Percy Green, who's on the fruit and veg in the market – lives in Crisp Street – told me some bloke had 'alf a dozen spring mattresses 'anging off 'is donkey cart and was shouting, "Wealth for the taking," as 'e wobbled by.'

Ernie couldn't help but laugh at his aunt in full swing and he could see Ada trying to hide a smile too.

'You laughing at me, boy?' Polly said, tongue-in-cheek. 'You're not too big for a thick ear, you know.'

The sight of such a tiny woman grabbing a wooden spoon and squaring up to her strapping nephew had everyone in stitches. Daisy and her sisters pretended to join in too and the place was soon in uproar, with Ada loving every minute of it.

After a bite to eat it was time for the couple to leave. Polly was well aware that her sister Nance would be eagerly waiting for her chance to meet the young lady who had caught Ernie's eye.

'The Lear's take a bit of getting used to,' Ernie said, squeezing Ada's hand as they found a seat on the tram. 'It'll be quieter in the shop, there's only Aunt Nance and George.'

Ada looked out of the grimy window as they made their way down Beckton Road. The surrounding streets seemed crammed together, but soon gave way to allotments and the occasional farm. Just as she was thinking East Ham wasn't too bad, a mixture of unpleasant smells filled her nostrils. With nothing but swampland ahead they turned down Manor Way and past a tar and liquor works. Ada was used to the string of cement works along Northfleet's riverside. They were a blot on the landscape, but here, the gasometers, oil tanks and pitch beds of the Gas Light and Coke Company's Works were never ending.

'So was it your Aunt Nance that took you and your brother in?' she asked as they were walking along Beaconsfield Street. 'But you lived here with your parents too, didn't you?'

'Yes, at number 10,' sighed Ernie. 'That's where we were when they all went in the workhouse. Bill and I ran to the shop in Cyprus Place. Look, Ada, I need to tell you something. It's been playing on my mind.'

Somewhat taken aback, Ada braced herself.

'You know I told you that my father died in the workhouse? Well, that's not true. 'E took 'is own life on Beckton Marshes. Leastways, that's what I was told. Couldn't cope with things no more.' Ernie hung his head, worried what Ada's response would be.

'Oh, Ernie, you should have got it off your chest before,' she whispered in his ear after kissing his cheek. 'I'm so sorry. It must have been awful. You know I've nothing but respect for how you've turned out.'

'I owe it all to Cyprus Place,' Ernie said, taking Ada's arm. 'Without Aunt Nance it would 'ave been very different. That's 'er shop on the corner, where it says *Camp Coffee* and *Barclay's Lager* on the side wall.'

'Well, I'll be blowed, if it isn't young Ernest,' Nance chirped from behind the counter. 'And who's this lovely lady on your arm?'

While introductions were being made, Ada was struck by how much aunt and nephew were alike. Their eyes had the same playful glint, and it wasn't long before they were teasing one another. Poor George, trying to count up his football pool coupons, came in for a ribbing too.

With its dark wooden shelves heaving with Wild Woodbines, Navy Cut, Gold Flake and dozens of other brands of tobacco, the shop was a smoker's paradise. Sales of cigarettes had accelerated rapidly since the war started, and at five for a penny, it meant that most working men smoked more than they drank.

'More ciggies than sweets in 'ere now,' said George as he watched Ada looking around. 'Especially since the Post Office lets people send 'em to the troops cheaply. Come through and 'ave a seat at the back, I'll put the kettle on.'

Ducking under the flypapers dangling down over the counter, it was a further challenge to squeeze past the tins of fruit, jars of syrup and bags of molasses piled high behind the door.

'Some things don't change in this family,' Ernie said, winking at his aunt.

Ada chatted happily on the tram back to the station. She'd enjoyed the day and both families had made her feel very much at home. Ernie was delighted that it had gone so well. It had been an important step for him, and he was mightily relieved.

Letting his mind wander for a brief second, he thought about his siblings and how he was going to tell them about his plans. Building bridges was proving harder with some more than others. Fred and Joe were away at sea, but at least Joe replied to his letters. He'd seen the girls as often as he could, and even timid Betsy was coming round. Harry was going to be the hardest nut to crack. He'd got married at eighteen and had a son a few weeks later. The boy was nearly two now, but Polly still hadn't seen him.

Feeling his arm being shaken, Ernie was abruptly brought back from his thoughts.

'You've not been listening to me, have you?' Ada smiled. 'Here I am saying how lovely your family are and you're in a world of your own.'

The late evening train carriage was empty – as Ernie hoped it would be. It was the moment he'd been waiting for. Sliding off the seat and going down on one knee, he produced a small box he'd been turning over and over in his pocket. For a second Ada thought he was mucking about, until she saw his eyes.

'Will you marry me?' he asked, opening the box and presenting it to her.

'Oh, Ernie…' she gasped, leaning back with both hands covering her face. 'It's beautiful.' She picked up the diamond ring and slid it onto her finger. 'I thought you'd never ask,' she said with tears in her eyes.

SATURDAY, 2ND OCTOBER 1915

It seemed like an age before the photographer had all the guests in position in the back garden. Bill Stone had given up worrying about his flower beds being trampled and his wife was keeping tight-lipped over the prospect of muddy boots trooping through her spotless kitchen. Everyone was relieved it wasn't raining, especially the women who were all wearing their Sunday best hats. Once the back two rows were perfectly placed, the photographer got to work on the seated row and finally on the little bridesmaids who were to kneel on a blanket laid across the gritted path. After a final check that bouquets and buttonholes were all in place and that no grimaces were likely to spoil anyone's countenance, the official photograph of Ernie and Ada Pridmore's wedding was taken.

It had been several hours since the ceremony at Holy Trinity Church, so everyone was peckish. The bridesmaids were only too happy to run and get sandwiches while matrons of honour Daisy and Mary Lear took all the bouquets inside for safekeeping. Ernie still couldn't get over how beautiful all the girls had looked carrying their white spider chrysanthemums, especially his bride with her veil falling from a mass of smaller flowers secured to her hair.

'Ada looks a treat,' declared Polly as she watched her nephew standing quietly, still taking it all in. 'It means a lot to me that she 'ad my two eldest at 'er side, especially since she's got plenty of relations of 'er own.'

It was certainly true that Ada had a large family, but she'd been careful to make the Stone and Pridmore sides look as even as she could in the church. With many of the men away at war, or unable to leave their jobs, it came as a pleasant surprise when Ernie heard that his brother Joe had been given a few days' leave from his ship, HMS *Marshal Soult*, which was on bombardment duties along the Belgian Coast. His sister Lily, now in service, had been given the weekend off too, so both stayed at the shop with Nance. It was the first time that brother and sister had seen one another since they were children and both only had sketchy memories of the family, so Polly, Jim and Nance did their best to fill in the gaps on the train to Gravesend. Ernie had been delighted to see them entering the church and made the snap decision to ask Mary's new husband to step aside and allow Joe to be his best man.

Try as they might to avoid talking about the war, it was never far from everyone's lips and, inevitably, the recent Zeppelin attacks over both London and Gravesend entered the conversation. Jim Lear related how he saw his first ever airship when one flew over his roof before dropping incendiaries on Hackney and Stratford. It was frightening and killed seven people. Bill Stone, driven outside by the noise of engines one night in June, saw his Zep blocking out the stars in a cloudless sky. It came as a terrible shock to see the nearby hospital nurses' quarters on fire. Bombs fell on Windmill Hill, Wrotham Road, Arthur Street and Cobham Street, and Hilda and Mabel told how an incendiary dropped in Brandon Street, landing on a stable, killing two horses. The more they swapped stories the greater the camaraderie between the two families seemed to grow.

With an autumn chill in the air and no room for the guests to mingle inside, the bride changed into her going-away outfit as soon as the sun started to go down. Everyone lined up in the street, hankies at the ready, to wave the couple off in the direction of the station. Bill Stone handed his handkerchief to his wife to dry her eyes on.

Not long after, holding hands in the gloomy carriage, Ernie gave his wife a tender kiss. They couldn't have wished for a better day and were very much looking forward to starting their life together after their honeymoon weekend in Margate. As luck would have it, 10 Bernard Street had come up for rent. Ernie had had to endure a load of mickey-taking about moving in next-door-but-one to his mother-in-law, but it didn't bother him.

As darkness finally fell, the train lights came on, making Ada jump and Ernie laugh.

'Well, at least you can read this now,' she said, pulling an envelope out of her purse. 'It came this morning.' Ernie's face dropped on seeing a telegram.

'Oh, my love, it's not bad news,' his new bride reassured him. Unfolding the paper with some trepidation, Ernie saw the message was from Fred sending them his congratulations and apologising for not being at the wedding. It didn't say where he was, of course, but Ernie knew from Aunt Polly that he was serving on the cruiser HMS *Europa* – the flagship at Moudros Bay participating in the Dardanelles campaign.

SATURDAY, 1ST JULY 1916

Ada and Ernie were settling into married life well. Like all brides, Ada had left her job before her wedding, so her two young sisters spent as much time as they were allowed at number 10. She would try shooing them home when Ernie came in from work, but they loved the way he teased them and made every excuse to stay. Nicknaming them 'Thursday and Friday' and untying their hair ribbons only made them want to come back for more. In truth, though, once she knew for certain that she was pregnant, Ada was only too glad of their help. As of 25th May, conscription had been extended to include married men, and although Ernie had been declared exempt due to being in a reserved occupation, there was no way of knowing if the situation might change.

The War was starting to affect everyone. Following Lord Kitchener's rallying call for volunteers to join his new armies, over three million men had signed up during the first two years of hostilities. By the summer of 1915 the number had begun to slow down. With casualties rising – two hundred and fifty thousand in Gallipoli alone – the recruitment campaign was stepped up

Much to Polly's anguish, her youngest son felt compelled to join up. In a few short weeks Ordinary Seaman Edgar Lear had arrived at the Naval training establishment Pembroke 1, and in February he transferred to the battleship HMS *Hibernia* which was on the Northern Patrol, preventing the enemy from attacking allied shipping and blockading goods from entering Germany. Jim kept such information to himself for fear of adding to his wife's bad nerves.

It soon became clear, however, that the numbers entering military service were still insufficient. The Government had no choice but to bring in conscription and so from March 1916, single men aged between eighteen and forty were liable to be called up. Polly had to endure watching another son, William, setting off for the Front. Having enlisted as a private in the Royal Army Medical Corps, she couldn't bear to think what horrors he would be experiencing.

Ernie had already had his first taste of warfare. On 26th February, during severe gales, the P&O passenger steamship SS *Maloja* was guided out of Tilbury en route to Bombay. The following morning, approaching the Strait of Dover at full speed, the ship overtook the Canadian collier *Empress of Fort William*, bound for Dunkirk with a cargo of 3,500 tons of coal. Suddenly a large explosion rocked the *Maloja*. She had struck a German mine laid by a U-boat and started to sink. The collier immediately went full ahead to assist but struck another mine. Within forty minutes both vessels had sunk with a loss of 155 lives.

Tragedies like these were happening daily. For over a year German U-boats had been attacking merchant vessels in British waters. In the early phase of submarine warfare, they ordered crews off the ships before sinking them with gunfire rather than torpedoes. But the torpedoing of the ocean liner *Lusitania* with the loss of so many lives – many of them American – introduced a more brutal aspect to the War. Germany feared bringing the United States into the conflict and for a while imposed rules requiring U-boats to surface when confronting liners, but this put the submarines themselves at risk and it wasn't long before the practice was abandoned.

At least the Royal Navy was there to protect our shipping and to defend our shores – or so everyone believed until the disaster at Jutland sixty miles off the coast of Denmark. Ernie was still reeling from the news that over six thousand British sailors had lost their lives on the last day of May when three seemingly indestructible battlecruisers of the Grand Fleet, HMS *Invincible*, HMS *Queen Mary* and HMS *Indefatigable*, were sunk after enemy shells exploded their magazines. The *Invincible* went down with its one thousand-man crew *ninety seconds* after it was hit by shellfire. Only a handful of men from the ships survived. The German Navy had been instructed to lure out and destroy part of the vastly superior British Grand Fleet in the North Sea in order to break the economic blockade that was strangling the German war effort and causing severe hardship amongst its population.

Neither side could claim outright victory from the battle and as the true scale of the losses began to filter through, the British press turned on the Navy, criticising it for failing to achieve a decisive outcome. When the battered ships of the fleet limped home to port, sailors found themselves being booed. Ernie felt for the men on HMS *Thunderer* which had taken part in the battle. Watching her being built at Thames Ironworks in Canning Town, he'd then been amongst the cheering crowd as she passed Gravesend on her maiden voyage.

But that was back in peacetime. So much had happened since then. Now, Tilbury dock was a hive of activity with supplies of every kind being loaded for shipment to the different theatres of war. Ernie could sense the urgency of the situation on the Western Front as he watched three-tier ambulance trains being loaded for delivery to France. They're expecting it to get a lot worse, he thought.

For young men like Private William Lear, what they witnessed on the first day of the Somme Offensive would be seared into their memories for the rest of their lives. On this day, 1st July, after a week-long artillery bombardment of the German lines, British troops advancing across open land found that the German defences had not been destroyed as expected and came under withering crossfire and shelling. The casualties were appalling. Many of the men who died had volunteered for Army service in 1914 and 1915, including the 'Pals' battalions made up of friends, relatives and workmates from the same communities. After a year of training, most had only got to the Western Front by early 1916 and, unlike professional soldiers, had little or no battlefield experience. Up against hardened German resistance from heavily defended positions, the result was nothing short of a massacre. By the end of the first day British forces suffered 57,470 casualties, of whom 19,240 were killed – the worst day in the history of the British Army.

SUNDAY, 24ᵀᴴ SEPTEMBER 1916

'Sounds like the airship's been 'it by the guns at Beckton,' shouted George down the stairs to his mother. 'Made several turns so it must 'ave been lost. Losing 'eight now.'

'I can 'ear bombs going off and the warning whistle blowing,' Nance shouted back.

'Got to drop its load to shed weight. Going the other way now, towards Chelmsford. Reckon you're safe to come up to bed now, Ma.'

Unbeknown to Nance, as she tossed and turned, unable to sleep, Zeppelin L33 – one of a twelve-Zeppelin raid on England that night – encountered more anti-aircraft fire and was finally forced to the ground in a village near Colchester. All twenty-two crew members managed to escape from the 650-foot airship whose buckled body now straddled a country lane. The German captain, Alois Bocker, attempted to warn those living in nearby cottages that he was going to set the Zeppelin on fire, but the terrified occupants refused to open their doors on hearing German voices. The men marched up the lane to the next village before being apprehended and handed over to the military.

Of the other eleven airships, L32 and L31 headed for London. Crossing Purfleet at about one in the morning, L32, which had been delayed by engine problems, was picked out by searchlights. Second Lieutenant Frederick Sowrey, RFC, out on routine patrol in his BE2c fighter biplane, launched an attack. Firing three drums of incendiary ammunition into the body of the Zeppelin, he watched her explode in a ball of flame and plummet to the ground near Billericay. None of the crew survived.

Like her sister, Polly was also having a sleepless night. Approaching London from the south, L31 released its bombs, killing seven people and injuring twenty-seven more before crossing the river. The next explosions felt so close that the house shook. Polly had her work cut out trying to calm a terrified Alf while sending Jim down the street to make sure that their new daughter-in-law was alright.

'It's bad enough 'aving William back in them trenches after only a few days of wedded bliss, without the poor girl being stuck on 'er own during this,' she said, shoving her reluctant husband out the front door.

Nancy was on Polly's doorstep before anyone had had their breakfast. She'd heard that L31 had dropped ten bombs on Leyton and there were more victims. Luckily, Lily, Betsy and Ada Pridmore, all now in service there, turned out to be unharmed.

MONDAY, 11ᵀᴴ DECEMBER 1916

A loud knock on the door made both Ernie and Ada jump. 'Who the devil can that be at this time of night?' Ada asked, putting down her knitting and attempting to get up out of the chair.

'Stay put, love, I'll go,' said her husband, abandoning his tea. 'I told you to leave that mangle alone in your condition.' Ada, her baby due in two weeks, was only too pleased to obey this particular instruction. Away from the warmth of the range, Ernie shivered and grabbed his jacket before opening the front door. Expecting someone in PLA uniform telling him he was needed back at work, instead he found a young man in khaki.

'Are you Ernie Pridmore by any chance?' he said with an accent straight out of the films Ernie had seen at the cinema. 'I'm John, John Pridmore. Your cousin, I think. We met some years ago in Cyprus Place.'

Taken aback, Ernie remained silent, trying to place the poor boy's face.

'We kicked a ball about… on some allotments, I think.'

'Well, I never. I remember. You were living with the Bateman family. You certainly didn't get that accent by staying in St Luke's Square, that's for sure. Where 'ave you come from?'

'Ontario in Canada. I went there not long after we met… It's a long story.'

'I'll be blowed,' said Ernie, scratching his head. 'You'd better come in or you'll freeze.'

152

After some left-over stew and a glass of beer, John explained that he'd only been in England since the 20th November. He'd come over on the SS *Olympic* with the 147th Battalion of the Canadian Expeditionary Force and was now stationed at Shoreham camp. Given a six-day pass before starting rifle training for the Front, he thought he would head back to the East End and see if he could find any of his proper family. He'd always remembered the shop and found it again easily. Nance had made him feel very welcome, so he'd stayed there for a couple of days, wandering around old haunts in Canning Town. He'd got Ernie's address from her.

By the time he'd related the whole story of going into the workhouse when the Batemans left for Canada, then being sent to Canada himself as a 'home boy', Ada was struggling. He spoke so fast and in such an unfamiliar accent that it was difficult for her to understand, but she could see her husband was taking it all in.

The bones of it were that John had remained with the Hammond family ever since Chester had picked him out of the line-up of boys when he was twelve. He'd been lucky: they were a God-fearing, abstemious family who treated him well. Another boy from a neighbouring farm was called 'street rat' by his master and told to make himself scarce if anyone visited.

John had learned a great deal about farming in Ontario from Patrick Hammond and felt bad about leaving him in the lurch seeing as he was now in his seventies. Patrick would have none of it, though, and encouraged John to go. He said that it would make a man of him and when he got back, he would help him choose a piece of land to farm for himself. Respecting Patrick as he did, John had initially put him down as his next of kin on his enlistment papers.

Right from the start, most Canadians had wanted to support the mother country and there was a degree of urgency to sign up recruits. In May 1915, Chester had driven the family to Owen Sound where his mother said she'd never seen so many people. A seven thousand-strong crowd watched a huge parade with four bands send off the 37th Battalion of the CEF. The Hammond farmhouse then turned itself into a hive of fundraising with Ellen sewing and knitting for all she was worth and holding parties to pack shipping parcels for the boys overseas.

Six months later, Grey County's own 147th battalion was formed. John enlisted at the end of November and began training, for which he received fifty cents a day. It was while he was marching round the streets of Owen Sound that he first met Stella Moore.

'It was at the monthly horse fair at the Queen's Hotel,' John reminisced, not quite sure what to make of the tapioca pudding he'd just been given. 'She and her mother have a stud farm and all the local horses are bought to go overseas these days, well, all except white or grey ones. They're getting good money for them.'

He turned towards Ada, whom he could see was now giving him her full attention.

'We started to go in the Tipperary Tearoom when I got time off and, gee, I knew right away that Stella was the girl for me. We're going to tie the knot as soon as this is all over. I've made her mother Jeanette my next of kin now, so they'll know straight away if I get injured or anything.'

Ada had to fight back the tears. She buried herself in her knitting so that he couldn't see her face. It was so romantic, and she hoped with all her heart that their marriage would go ahead, but she and Ernie had recently been to the pictures and what she had seen there had left its mark. *The Battle of the Somme*, an official feature-length film showing soldiers in action at the Front, had been playing in the cinemas since August and millions of people had already seen it. When on 18th November Commander in Chief, Sir Douglas Haig, called a halt to the Somme operation claiming that the offensive had achieved its objectives in 'holding the German forces and wearing down the enemy's strength on the Western Front', many people simply didn't believe it. For the families of the 146,000 British and Dominion soldiers killed and two hundred thousand injured, being told that their sacrifice to gain just six miles in territory had not been in vain, was a bitter pill to swallow. Given what she now knew, Ada feared for John's safety.

They both wanted John to stay in Bernard Street for the rest of his pass. His experiences in Canada were fascinating and with Ernie doing his best to fill in the gaps in his past, for the first time in nineteen years, John felt he was truly a cog in the Pridmore wheel. Most of what he learned about his mother was disappointing and it was painful to discover that he had two half-sisters who'd not only been put in the same workhouse but also ended up in Canada.

Ernie thought it possible that Aunt Nance would know where Eliza lived, but John wasn't at all sure he wanted to know.

'I can understand how you feel,' Ernie agreed, 'but one thing Nance told me years ago keeps coming back to me. Eliza was adamant that she 'ad you baptised before you went to the Batemans. She seemed to care enough about you 'aving 'er name.'

John shrugged his shoulders. 'You're about to be a father, Ern. Can you imagine giving your child away?'

'Of course not, but things were a lot different for Eliza. I'm not sure she 'ad any choice.' Ernie pondered his words, aware that he hadn't addressed his own mother's abandonment of her children and subsequent disappearance. 'Come on,' he said, standing up and throwing John his overcoat. 'All this talk of me becoming a father is making me thirsty. Might be the last chance I'll 'ave of getting a pint of mild and bitter down the Pier Tavern for a while. You can tell me more about what you'll be getting up to at Shoreham.'

Huddled near the fire, pints in hand, John related how his battalion had joined the 158th (Vancouver), 180th (Ontario), the 194th (Edmonton Highlanders), signallers and artillery on board the trans-Atlantic liner *Olympic* at Halifax, Nova Scotia. There were plenty of jokes about it being her thirteenth crossing as a troopship, especially since she was the sister ship of the ill-fated *Titanic*, but everyone remained in great spirits. The voyage had, thankfully, been calm and John was grateful for a canvas hammock as it took five days to reach Ireland and a further night waiting in the Irish Sea for the tide to be right to allow them to dock at Liverpool. They then travelled south on packed trains to Shoreham, where the camp could be summed up in one word – muddy. There was a lot of squad drilling going on in the pouring rain.

Shoreham had been chosen as the site for one of the training camps for Kitchener's New Army. Erected on open farmland, at first the men lived in tents, but within six months a huge town of huts was constructed, complete with a canteen, chapel, post office and social clubs. In 1916 the site became a base for Canadian troops as well as British, expanding into two distinct camps: Mill Hill for recruits and Slonk Hill for advanced soldiering.

Every day started with the sound of reveille at half past six and ended with lights out just after half past nine. There were frequent medical examinations which John passed easily, being extremely fit and strong. Many men failed, however, and were despatched off home, their tail between their legs. He wrote to Mrs Hammond telling her that he missed her cooking and the taste of butter. On the whole, though, army grub wasn't bad; there just wasn't enough of it.

'So what will you be doing when you get back?' Ernie asked.

'We're straight on the ranges,' John replied, wiping his mouth after a gulp of beer. 'Two weeks indoors with blanks, then outside with real bullets. After that we get issued with a Lee Enfield rifle and one of those long bayonets which you need for trench warfare.'

Ernie shuddered at the thought of it and counted his blessings that he was in a reserved occupation.

'Eventually we'll be heading for Slonk Hill which they've transformed into a realistic battleground with trenches and barbed wire just like we're going to find on the Front. Be our first experience with machine guns and mortars. They say we'll be going in February.'

The few days that they'd spent together seemed to fly by and it had been an unexpected pleasure. At the station John threw his kit bag into the carriage, shook Ernie's hand and kissed Ada on the cheek.

'Look after that baby when it comes,' he said cheerfully, slamming the train door shut and opening the window as the whistle blew. Waving until John disappeared into the distance, Ernie was bursting with pride. 'What a courageous young man,' he said, holding Ada's hand.

They both walked quietly back home engrossed in thought. Ada hoped she'd hear that attractive Canadian accent again someday, perhaps with Stella by his side. Ernie wondered if Eliza ever thought about her son that had been sent to live thousands of miles away and was now heading for the Western Front.

FRIDAY, 19TH JANUARY 1917

Nance and Polly clinked their glasses together and drained the last few drops of their port and lemons. 'Bit of good news, at last, eh?' said Nance with a sigh.

'Just what we needed to cheer us all up,' agreed her sister as she folded the letter and replaced it in its envelope. They'd been reading Ada's latest account of sleepless nights and endless washing following the birth of their newest nephew, Ernest Junior.

Glancing at her watch, Nance suddenly realised the time. 'Poll, it's gone 'alf six and I need to get George 'is tea.'

'Gracious, is it really? *I'd* better be off too or Jim'll send out a search party.'

Just as Nance was opening the shop door to let her sister out, a blast of air threw her violently back inside. Both sisters instinctively fell to the floor and covered their ears as a huge explosion made the ground shake and the electric lights flicker.

'You two alright?' shouted George, bursting in from the back yard. 'Both bedroom windows are blown out and there's smashed glass all along Cyprus Place.'

'What the bloody 'ell's 'appened?' yelled Nance. Feeling her legs shaking, she held onto the counter. 'Is it the Germans?'

'Dunno, but there's a red glow in the sky and I can see smoke pouring out of Silvertown.'

'Daisy!' screamed Polly. 'I've got to get 'ome to see if she's alright.'

'I'm coming with you,' said George, helping her up. 'Not letting you go on your own. Don't worry, though, Daisy will 'ave clocked off two 'ours ago.'

'No, she's been working lates – doing 'er bit till nearly bedtime since Bill's been at sea. If the Germans are dropping bombs she could be in the thick of it. They'll be after the Arsenal and the shells for our troops.'

Daisy Turrell had been 'doing her bit' ever since she and fifty thousand other participants in the Women's War Pageant marched along the embankment to Whitehall on a rainy Saturday in July 1915. Holding banners proclaiming *Shells made by a Wife may save her Husband's Life* and *A Woman's Battle Cry is Work, Work, Work* they were there to impress upon the Minister of Munitions their willingness to help in war service. As a result, women were now filling jobs that had traditionally only been open to men.

Straight after Bill had been called up, Daisy went to work at the Royal Ordnance Factory at Woolwich Arsenal where a third of the huge workforce was now women. Making shells, artillery and gun carriages was extremely dangerous but she knew it was essential work and for the first time, she felt valued.

'I'm much 'appier calling you a Munitionette than a Suffragette,' her father told her. 'Lily's got a new job too, 'ave you 'eard? Bus conductress. Dunno what Ernie'll say about 'is sister becoming one of them.'

Daisy shook her head; her father was still stuck in the past. ''E won't say anything, Pa. Women are doing a lot of jobs they've never done before, or weren't considered capable of, more like. You're going to 'ave to get used to it, because it's 'ere to stay.'

It was true: former domestic servants like Lily, made up nearly half of the 1,700 women who, by the end of 1916, had become bus conductresses. The Bank of England now employed women clerks and office work was opening up a new world for young women whose sights were set on things their mothers could never have imagined.

Thankfully George was right, he and Polly found Daisy at home and unharmed. She'd got the kettle on, knowing her mother would be round to check.

'Course we were worried, Ma, the blast made our two solid-iron factory gates shut all by themselves,' she said while trying to replace hair pins fallen out during the rush to get away. 'A policeman told me to go straight 'ome and stay indoors. Seems there's a massive fire in Silvertown, nothing left of Brunner Mond and Vanesta's plywood. A couple of ships in the dock are on fire and so is the flour mill.'

'Got to be the Germans,' declared Polly. 'They must 'ave known Brunner Mond was full of TNT.'

Polly wasn't the only one thinking like that. Everyone was frightened that the explosion had been caused by a bomb and they were fearful of what might follow in the days ahead. There'd been no official statement and there was nothing in the papers yet.

With a crippling shell shortage, the War Office needed to find chemical plants that could service the war effort. Brunner Mond had spare capacity since it ceased to produce caustic soda and so it was chosen to purify TNT. The chief scientist at the factory described the purification process as 'manifestly very dangerous'. Despite this and the fact that the factory was situated in a highly populated area, the plant had been producing TNT round the clock, since September 1915.

On the evening of 19th January, a fire broke out in the melt-pot room, spreading to the stores of TNT, much of it in railway wagons awaiting transport. Fifty tonnes exploded, completely destroying the building and nine other factories and mills nearby. More than sixty thousand properties suffered blast damage, including Silvertown fire station opposite, and millions of windows were shattered in surrounding areas.

People reported hearing the blast from as far away as Norfolk, while molten metal cascaded for several miles, some damaging a gasometer in Greenwich and causing a giant fireball.

Several firemen were amongst the seventy-four who died, with four hundred more maimed or injured in streets that were busy due to a change of shift at seven p.m. The upstairs rooms of houses had suffered the most damage, twelve of the deaths being babies or toddlers who'd already been put to bed for the night. One poor man lost his wife and four children that way. Polly heard later that her friend's young granddaughter had lost an arm carrying flasks and food baskets to her parents who were working overtime. With three thousand people living within a quarter of a mile of the factory, everyone knew someone who had been affected.

Nance knew she was going to have to wait a long time before her windows could be replaced as six hundred new homes were now needed, with even more requiring structural repairs. Daisy Parsons, having set up a Mother and Child Welfare Centre in West Ham, wrote furious letters to those authorising the rebuilding of the area. Calling the living conditions the 'Scandal of Silvertown', she argued that damp, unhealthy dwellings were responsible for numerous cases of croup and rickets and that without real improvements these would continue to take their yearly toll.

And if all this wasn't bad enough, people were starting to complain about fuel rationing, and food shortages were causing real hardship.

FRIDAY, 9TH MARCH 1917

'Says in the *Sketch* that this has been *the coldest winter on record*, Ern,' Ada said, suddenly feeling the need to put more coal on the range.

''Ope you're counting 'ow many lumps you're chucking on there,' Ernie responded cheerily. 'I've 'ad to register with the coalman now – *to be sure of getting an allocation*,' he added in a posh voice.

Ada was on her high horse. 'This voluntary rationing of food is worse. It's bad enough being told to leave out meat on some days, but a stingy twelve ounces of sugar a week goes nowhere. You have two sugars in your tea for a start and young Ern's ready to be weaned. Babies only go on solids if it's sweet.'

The truth is that German submarines were doing serious damage to merchant shipping and essential supplies coming in from abroad were often finishing up at the bottom of the sea. Forty-six thousand tons of meat had already been lost in 1917, along with eighty-five thousand tons of sugar, causing soaring food prices and panic buying.

'Can't be 'elped, love, and I reckon it'll become compulsory soon,' said Ernie, trying to put a comforting arm around his wife, but she wasn't having any of it.

'That'll make things better, not worse,' she declared, surprising her husband. 'Won't be none of this hoarding nonsense. I go in David Greigs every week and I see them women buying their regulation two pound of chops and sausages. Then, after they've got their veg in the market, they're back in Greigs buying *another* string of sausages. That Mrs Bennet's the worst. She won't be able to do it if she's got a ration card.'

Hands on hips and oozing with indignation, Ada went to the front door to pick up the letter she'd just heard land on the mat. Looking at it carefully, she turned it over in her hands. 'Ernie, it's for you. It's got one of them red military stamps on it...'

February 28th

Hello Ernie,

Well, here I am finally in France! I'm now with the 4th CMR and we arrived in strength on the 22nd. Wish I could say I was strolling down the Champs Elysees, but no such luck. I'm sitting in my billet where once there were farms so I should feel at home – hard to tell that from how it looks now, though. Constant rain doesn't help, of course. Usual brigade route marches and drilling goes on here, Ern, but we've also had training on the Lewis gun, rifle grenades, sniping and bayonet fighting. Thankfully we got a bit of a breather last night when our bombing squad was awarded a prize for winning the divisional competition, we all got some extra ciggies.

Saw Bish Bishop yesterday, don't know if you remember me talking about the flying ace that comes from Owen Sound, but he's a real star around here. Turns out he was searching for German airships over London last September so he might have had a hand in bringing down one of the Zeps that caused Aunt Nance all that worry!

Well, I hope all is well in the docks, Ernie, and with Ada, of course. Gee, nearly forgot to mention Ernie Jnr! Won't be long before he'll be playing football with his pa.

All the best,

John

John Pridmore had transferred to the 4th Canadian Mounted Rifles on 17th February 1917. Despatched a few days later, the Battalion finally arrived at Burbure, Northern France, on the 26th. At the peak of fitness, his endurance was now about to be tested with physical training, drill and combat exercises in the woods and practice trenches.

His letters kept coming.

March 15th

Hello Cousin,

I am writing this in a real dugout, this time near the front line so please forgive the scribbling. Life seems to be upside down – working nights and sleeping during the day. Me and my mates sleep on the steps squashed like sardines. Things are still quiet with us, but we'll probably be seeing some action soon.

Tell Ada not to worry. No, we never wear body shields. They're too heavy and I already have as much as I can carry. If you could see me with it all on you'd laugh. Do you remember the nice new uniform I wore when last you saw me? Well, it doesn't look the same now, it's caked in mud. Sometimes my boots are so heavy, I can hardly lift them. You can't avoid it – in some places you're up to your knees in it and you gather up even more from the sides of the trenches as you walk along them.

We have wonderful fireworks every night and the guns are going constantly, so things are never dull.

All the best,

John

John's first taste of real action came on 18th March when his unit set off for the front line to relieve the 60th Canadian Infantry Battalion. Ernie told Ada that he seemed to be taking it all in his stride.

Quite a lot of things have happened since I last wrote to you. We marched to just a few miles from the line

*and were then told to rest in a field. Can't remember
the last time I saw green grass! We even played a bit
of football in the sunshine. Not up to your standard,
though, Ernie.*

*We slept there that night and started early morning for
the line. They gave us a good breakfast then sent us over
the top before we had time to think about it. Just as well,
really, as we came under fire from the long-range guns
straight away and later the rifle. The noise is deafening,
machine-gun bullets whistle round you as you go on in
little rushes, taking cover in between. No shortage of shell
holes for that!*

*Next day, the enemy positions got bombarded and
then we advanced again. A mine was blown to the left our
front but thankfully no effort was made by Fritz to occupy
the crater! I'll tell you a lot more someday, but there isn't
space here. Anyway, our Battalion did well and I am out
of it without a scratch.*

By 1st April John and his fellow soldiers were at Villers-au-Bois
resting in preparation for the 'big push' that everyone knew was
coming. Four divisions of the Canadian Expeditionary Force
had been allotted the unenviable task of capturing the heavily
defended high ground on Vimy Ridge to the north of the Arras
sector. Its capture was essential to support the thrust by the
British Third Army to the south.

Following the disastrous losses on the Somme in 1916,
a strategic plan for a major spring offensive, involving over a
million French and British troops, had been advanced by the
French Commander in Chief, who believed that a massive assault
in central France could overwhelm German resistance, leading
to early victory in the War. The Germans, however, recognising
the danger, withdrew to the fortified Hindenburg Line, forcing
Allied Commanders to alter their plans. The British mounted a
diversionary attack in the Arras sector designed to draw German
reserve troops away from where the French planned their main

offensive. For the Canadians who had been preparing for the assault, zero hour was approaching fast.

April 8th

Dear Ernie,

Just a few lines before we go over the top tomorrow. We're resting in our billets after days of wire cutting. Weather's been good today but I hear it's going to be blowing a gale tomorrow.

Bishop's been made a flight commander so I feel a bit happier knowing him and his pals will be paving the way for us.

Anyway, Ern, I've given my Stella your address just in case she needs it. I hope you don't mind but I think of you now as 'my next-of-English-Kin'.

Love to all,
John

At five thirty a.m. on Easter Monday, 9th April, whistles blew and the British 3rd and 5th armies attacked along a fifteen-mile front near the town of Arras. The four Canadian divisions advanced together against Vimy Ridge under constant bombardment and machine-gun fire. After two hours of heavy fighting, the 4th Canadian Mounted Rifles had occupied the enemy front line and support trenches.

Having secured their positions, a patrol was sent out to Petit Vimy on the 10th where a force of Germans with a machine gun was discovered in the sunken road to La Folie Wood. This was bombarded, clearing a way for the forward troops. On the 11th, John's unit was ordered to dislodge the enemy from a trench system on the reverse side of the Vimy Ridge slope, during which time the Canadians were heavily shelled. By the night of the 11th the Battalion had held the line for sixty-five hours without blankets, greatcoats or much in the way of sleep, when they were finally relieved by fellow Canadians in the midst of a snowstorm.

The battle for Vimy Ridge proved a decisive, though costly, victory which helped to turn the tide of the War. Sadly, 3,600 Canadians died and seven thousand were wounded. The 4th Canadian Mounted Rifles lost sixty-two men in the actions of 9th, 10th and 11th April with eighty-two wounded.

SATURDAY, 28TH APRIL 1917

It was the words *Canada Postage* that made Ada look at the stamp more closely. The handwriting on the envelope was unfamiliar too. They hadn't heard from John for three weeks and were beginning to worry.

'Ernie...' she said quietly as she handed the letter to her husband, 'it's from Canada. I hope it's not bad news.'

Ernie studied the handwriting and turned the letter over carefully. Even if John had been wounded, he wouldn't have been sent home yet, so perhaps this was from his sweetheart, Stella, who had heard something from him.

Ada leaned over the armchair as Ernie unfolded the letter:

> *Newlands Farm,*
> *Park Head, Ontario*
> *18th April 1917*

Dear Ernest,

> *It is with very great sorrow that I have to inform you that your cousin John was killed in action at Vimy Ridge, in France, on 11th April. I felt duty bound to write and tell you of this tragic news as John made me his next of kin prior to setting off for England.*

> *We first heard that he had been wounded and hoped for the best, but you can imagine how distraught my daughter Stella became once the information was*

corrected and confirmed that he had in fact been killed.

I wanted you to know that John was extremely well liked by everyone in our family and we had become very fond of him. He was kind and thoughtful to Stella and they were a devoted couple. I was only too happy to give them my blessing when I heard they were planning to get married.

John never spoke a great deal about his childhood, but I know that he didn't have much stability and being dispatched off to a foreign country must have been distressing. It all makes his courage and fortitude seem all the more remarkable to me. The poor boy wrote a will before going to the front, leaving everything he had to Stella. This, it turns out, is just his uncollected pay, bless him.

Stella told me that he wrote enthusiastically about meeting you and your wife recently. I think making a connection with his English family was important to him and I am truly grateful that you made him feel welcome.

He will be missed, but rest assured not forgotten.

Yours sincerely,

Jeanette Moore

TUESDAY, 8TH MAY 1917

'Are you sure we're safe staying here, Ern?'

'Yes, love, I'm certain. All the crew that got it are off the ship now… one way or another, anyway. Reckon their bodies 'ave been buried pretty damn quick too.'

'Well, I'm not taking young Ernie along the prom, not until that ship's gone. I ain't survived a Boche bomb only to catch the plague!'

Ada hadn't been sleeping well since the SS *Sardinia* arrived in Gravesend with seven cases of bubonic plague aboard. The news had spread around the town like wildfire.

'She'll be 'eading back to the East soon,' reassured her husband. 'It's causing a lot of trouble at the dock, though. No one wants to 'andle the cargo.' Hearing a whimper, Ernie started rocking his son's crib in the hope he'd stay asleep a little longer. 'Shall we pay Aunt Nance a visit this weekend?'

'Be lovely,' answered Ada, giving her husband a fond kiss, 'but I know you only too well – you want to find out where that Aunt Eliza of yours is now living. It's been playing on your mind, hasn't it?'

'I just think she should be told what a brave lad 'er John turned out to be. I doubt she 'as a clue.'

'Hmm,' snorted Ada, taking over the rocking. 'None of it was down to her, that's for sure.'

Ernie stood outside 23 Kingston Road, Leytonstone, watching the net curtains move as he knocked firmly on the door. He'd already seen a child's grubby hand being snatched away so he wasn't going to give up. A woman pushing a milk delivery barrow confirmed that Eliza was indeed inside. 'I've just tried,' she said, grateful to stop for a minute a mop her brow. 'She owes *me* money too.' Clearly thinking Ernie was the rent collector, she carried on. 'I made the mistake of taking pity when 'er boy begged me for a pint of sterilised. Told me 'is mother would see me right on payday. Should 'ave guessed she don't 'ave no payday.'

Suddenly the door opened, revealing two young lads and an older girl trying to pull them aside to enable her to slam it shut again. Ernie realised he had to act fast. He stuck his boot in the door jam and shouted over the commotion. 'If Eliza Pridmore lives 'ere, tell 'er I'm a relation.'

Shoving the boys out of her way, the girl came closer and stared up at Ernie. Taking off his cap and bending down to her level, he said slowly, 'Is Eliza your mother?'

Without a word, the child skipped back to the scullery, leaving the boys kicking at Ernie's boot. Eventually a pregnant woman, in shabby clothes, came to the door. With no sign of recognition on either part, Ernie identified himself. 'I'm Ernie, your brother Joseph's son.'

Eliza looked at him carefully before glancing back over her shoulder. 'What are you doing 'ere?' she asked suspiciously. Taken aback, Ernie realised he wasn't going to be invited in. He also sensed a man lurking in the shadows, within earshot. Choosing his words carefully, he said quietly, 'I thought you should know that John 'as been killed in France, fighting for the Canadians.'

A flicker across Eliza's eyes told him that the news had registered, even though her expression hardly changed. 'I'm sorry to 'ear that,' she responded, managing to sound unaffected.

'I saw 'im a couple of months ago,' he continued. ''E was a brave young man. You'd be proud of 'im.'

'I'm proud of *all* our men,' said Eliza, taking a deep breath and turning sideways. She gestured to the figure behind her to come to the door. 'This is Charlie, my 'usband-to-be. 'E lost 'alf 'is leg on the Somme. Charlie, this is me nephew Ernie, 'e's come with bad news about someone else in our family.'

Charlie lent on the wall, enabling him to let go of his crutch so that the two men could briefly shake hands. 'Canadian, did I 'ear you say? Was that at Vimy Ridge?'

'Yes, 'e was only nineteen.' Ernie nodded, noticing that the man he was talking to was at least forty years of age.

'You PLA?' Charlie sniffed on recognising Ernie's uniform. 'Not experienced the Front yourself then?' Without waiting for an answer he turned and made his way back down the passageway, shutting the kitchen door behind him.

'Oh, don't mind 'im,' whispered Eliza. 'He ain't 'imself nowadays. Thanks for not spilling the beans about John. Charlie don't know nothing about me first three kids and these three ain't 'is either. Still, at least this one is.' She smiled, rubbing her hand over her bulge. 'I'm sorry to 'ear about John, but what's in the past 'as to stay in the past, if you get my meaning.'

Ernie was lost for words and started to turn away.

'When you next see Nance and Polly,' Eliza finished, closing the door, 'be sure and tell 'em I've finally got someone wanting to marry me. Doubt they thought that would ever 'appen. Bye.'

WEDNESDAY, 13ᵀᴴ JUNE 1917

Ernie stretched out on the deck of his PLA tug, where he'd recently been transferred, to make the most of the sunshine. Mugs of tea in hand, the crew opened their lunch bags, joking about the meagre offerings their wives had managed to scrape together that day. Having dug up the garden to grow vegetables, Ernie's pack-up always contained plenty of lettuce, though not much else.

Suddenly the *boom boom* of anti-aircraft guns disturbed their peace and quiet. Looking up across the Albert Dock, Ernie was amazed to see the sky filled with aircraft. No less than fourteen German Gotha heavy bombers were heading in their direction, low in the bright sky.

'Bloody hell!' shouted the tug's captain. 'Looks like we're in for it.' Before the men had time to act, a single bomb, sounding like a roar of thunder, hit one of the dockside warehouses, causing it to burst into flames. Several vans parked outside exploded simultaneously and a wooden railway truck was lifted high into the air shattering into splinters as it landed again. As they all ran to help put out the fires, Ernie could hear more bombs dropping nearby and immediately thought of Aunt Nance and George in Cyprus Place.

'There's two gone off close to Beckton, but none in Cyprus,' a fireman told him. 'Most of them will have been saved for the City.'

London's air defences were designed to combat zeppelins, which always operated at night, so they were virtually useless against raids by bombers, which aimed to terrorise the civilian population and lower morale to distract attention away from the Western Front.

Turning the corner of Ferndale Road, Ernie was relieved to see the Pridmore shop still intact with a queue outside that stretched up the street. He smiled at the old Packer's Chocolates awnings tied on the outside of the windows which he'd seen put up every year since he was a lad.

'Good to see you,' said George. 'Mum got in a right old tizz when that bomb dropped on the Albert. Thought you might be in the thick of it.'

'We did what we could,' said Ernie. 'Luckily the fire engines got there quick, but they reckon at least eight blokes got killed.'

'Thank God you're still in one piece,' declared Nance, appearing from the room at the back holding some of the tobacco they still had left. 'Two of them bombs only just missed the gas works and dropped on Alexandra Road instead. Thought we were gunna lose our windows again. Mrs Fletcher who lives in Savage Gardens says she's 'eard another forty 'ouses will need repairing.'

The newspapers were soon full of the story of the air raid where 162 people had been killed, 104 of them from the East End. The Imperial German Air Service had bombed numerous targets in London, including Fenchurch Street, Aldgate and Liverpool Street. Three of the seventy-two bombs which had been dropped within a mile radius of Liverpool Street station, were direct hits – one blowing apart a passenger train that was just about to leave.

But the worst was still to come. After bombing the City, the Gothas turned east for home. One, still carrying a 100lb bomb, dropped it on Upper North School in Poplar, smashing through the three-storey building packed with children and exploding on the ground floor. Eighteen infants died, with thirty others badly injured.

A week later, with the East End in mourning and the docks at a standstill, one of the biggest funerals ever seen in London was held for the children. Each coffin, covered in pink and white flowers, was carried to Poplar Parish Church by horse and carriage. Boy scouts and girl guides formed an aisle on the church steps, while cadets in khaki lined the road before and after the service. Fifteen of the children were buried in a mass grave at the East London Cemetery.

Ada was heartbroken, especially when she saw the photograph of school caretaker Benjamin Batt scrabbling through the rubble searching for survivors. While a little girl was pulled out alive three days later, among the bodies located was Batt's own son. Ada knew terrible things happened on battlefields, but to kill innocent children was an atrocity. As Ernie comforted her, he couldn't get the sight of those aircraft out of his mind. This was a different kind of warfare and if it could be waged from the skies, what did that mean for the future?

Pridmore's shop, Cyprus Place
© PLA Collection, Museum of London

MONDAY, 2ND JULY 1917

Nance stood outside West Ham register office waiting for the newlyweds to appear. Feeling a bit sheepish about being there since her motive was more curiosity than celebratory, she fully intended to stay for just a few minutes. But when the small group finally emerged, she found the obvious joy on Eliza's face irresistible.

Wearing a loose-fitting dress, which was entirely suitable given her condition, and arm in arm with Charlie in his army uniform and crutches, the pair looked the best they could, given the circumstances. Weddings were quite a different affair in these war-torn days, so no one walking by blinked an eyelid at the situation. Nance couldn't help but wonder what Sam would have made of it, though, had he still been alive. Here was his sister, nearly forty, getting married for the first time despite having had six children – mostly by different men – and with another on the way.

Not expecting to know anyone else in the gathering, Nance was surprised to see Henry Cook Pridmore, standing in the background. It hadn't occurred to her that he would make the trip from Wisbech, but there he was, trying to control Eliza's two wayward sons before the bridegroom stepped in and gave each one a clip round the ear, which only made things worse.

Ignoring what was going on behind her, when Eliza spotted Nance she waved enthusiastically. Without an official photographer and no one able to throw rice due to the shortages, there wasn't much point hanging around, so Charlie announced that they were adjourning to the British Lion for a pint and a sandwich. Nance was just about to dash off home, when Henry grabbed her arm. 'It's good to see a familiar face,' he smiled. 'Will you keep me company?'

With beer having gone up to fourpence a pint and war loaves made from rye and slushy potato, it was never going to be much of a wedding breakfast, particularly since the unpleasant-tasting blackish bread had to be at least twelve hours old before it could be sold.

'Don't exactly make you want to ask for more, that's for sure,' Henry said with a wink as Nancy waved away the plate on offer.

It was nice being together again. Nancy liked her father-in-law, and it was obvious his second wife was still looking after him well. Eliza had done nothing to endear herself to Maud, so she had no inclination to accompany Henry to West Ham. As a wheeler-dealer, giving up his marine stores had been hard, but he now seemed content to spend his remaining years in retirement.

Inevitably, the conversation turned to the War. Eliza had told her father about John being killed at Vimy Ridge, but he was pleased to find out from Nance that John had visited Ernie in Gravesend before leaving for France. He said he occasionally heard from Amelia Bateman in Canada – whom Nance remembered coming into her shop with John all those years ago. Having been originally given a free homestead in Swan River Valley, Manitoba, the Bateman family had tried to farm the land, but it turned out to be more swamp than soil. As a result, Amelia had moved nearer to Winnipeg where her sons were working on the railroad.

Nance could tell Henry was deeply saddened about not having had much of a relationship with his grandchildren. He doubted that he would visit the East End again.

WEDNESDAY, 6TH FEBRUARY 1918

Finally, after fifty years of campaigning, the Representation of the People Act granted women the right to vote in the next general election – providing they met certain criteria, namely that they had to be householders over the age of thirty, wives of householders, occupiers of property with an annual rent of five pounds or graduates of universities.

'I thought you'd be pleased,' sighed Polly, shaking her head.

'Oh, I am, Ma,' Daisy replied. 'It's just that it's still not *all* women who've got the vote.'

'*You'll* be able to after your birthday, though,' said Polly, slightly agitated. She'd been hoping that today's news would put an end to her daughter's obsession with Votes for Women, especially since she was expecting her first child.

'Yes, but Lily and Betsy and all those other women in service still won't be able to vote, even after they reach thirty.'

'Well, it's better than nothing,' her mother retorted, turning away.

With the War grinding on and a general election looming, deciding who got the vote had become a divisive issue for politicians. They knew that without the million women workers now employed in the munitions industry, the war could very easily be lost, and without those working on the land doing agricultural jobs formerly reserved for men, the

178

population might very well be starving. Four in ten of all women workers were married – something unheard of before 1914.

There was no serious debate about giving *all* women the vote, though, as by doing so they would have been in the majority due to the loss of men in the war – and that rang alarm bells in Parliament because it threatened to undermine traditional party representation in the House of Commons. You couldn't ignore the influence of the suffrage movement or the growing support for the Labour Party, but you could legislate to give *some* people the vote sooner, and the rest later.

What this meant was that all men over twenty-one – or nineteen, if they had seen active service – got the vote regardless of their property status. Women, on the other hand, had to be over thirty and able to meet certain property qualifications. It was clever politics because it looked like women were getting the vote in recognition of their role as defence workers. In fact, sixty per cent of women – including many who contributed in other ways to the war effort – were still unable to vote.

And that's what outraged Daisy. She'd been reading about pioneering women like Elsie Inglis – a suffragist doctor who, after having been turned down by the British Government, opened a hospital in France at the outbreak of war staffed entirely by women. Then there was Harriette Chick, a pioneering biochemist who had found ways of reducing infection in battlefield situations and of treating soldiers with nutritional deficiencies like scurvy and beriberi. Women were now active in the new science of psychotherapy and in the forefront of the treatment of shell shock. What else were they capable of achieving given the chance, she wondered?

'There'll be no men left soon,' Ernie said out loud on reading that the conscription age for military service was likely to be raised to fifty-one.

'I beg your pardon?' the young merchant seaman standing next to him said. They were at the bar of the Three Daws after a long day where Gravesend tugs had assisted the damaged cargo boat SS *Baron Napier* into Tilbury dock.

Ernie looked up from his newspaper and gave the lad his full attention. 'Sorry, son, talking to meself. Must 'ave been bad for you out there in the North Atlantic.'

'Storms are the worst. They do more damage than the U-boats. We lost far too many horses this time.'

Ike Thompson's armed merchant ship had been on the return journey from Halifax, Nova Scotia, with a consignment of horses destined for the Western Front when a force 10 storm broke, scattering the convoy and pounding the *Baron Napier* with massive waves.

'Poor bloody things,' Ike continued. 'The timber framework where they were tied up together was smashed to pieces, so they broke loose and careered around the deck for three days. Couldn't try to catch them, we'd have been washed overboard.'

'Yes, I saw the damage,' Ernie said, thinking back to mangled metal and shattered timbers he had seen earlier. ''Ow many did you lose?'

'Thirty, maybe more. The vet had to shoot the most seriously injured, then he and the cook went round selecting the best joints. We lived on horseflesh most of the way back.' Ernie smiled at the matter-of-factness of the description. Having lived on scraps of meat for the past four years, the thought of daily portions of horsemeat made his mouth water.

As he bought another drink for himself and the young man, the Thames tuggie looked around at the faces of the merchant ship's crew as they relaxed properly for the first time in weeks; he admired their stoicism in the face of what must have been constant danger at sea.

'Must be *hell* when the U-boats start taking pot-shots at you?'

'You don't have time to think about it,' Ike answered. 'It all happens so fast. On the last crossing on the way to Montreal we had a fight with a sub, shelling and being shelled with shrapnel for three hours. We were on our own mid-ocean, having split up the day before, and Fritz made some jolly good shots considering the roughness of the sea.' After a slurp of beer and seeing that Ernie was now engrossed in the story, Ike continued. 'It came up four thousand yards astern of us, just as it was getting light and fired two high explosives. Woke up all hands, but both missed, thank God. Me and Jack – over there – are gun crew. I put in the cartridges and Jack the projectiles. We grabbed our coats and raced to the platform. Could see the big 'U' on the conning tower and German ensign quite clearly. Our firing made it slow down a bit but then it started firing shrapnel, some bursting near us making a cloud of black smoke. We started zigzagging and lit smoke boxes to cover us. Meanwhile, all the commotion had brought the rats scurrying out and we had to kick them away to stop our boots being gnawed to pieces!'

'You look young to be on the gun platform, lad,' said Ernie. ''Ow old are you?'

'Nearly seventeen,' said Ike, taking another swig. 'We had a misfire or two which made Fritz come in closer thinking he'd killed us, but we started banging away again until about half past seven when he was either hit and sunk, or else he'd had enough and submerged. Then we all went and had breakfast.'

Ernie shook his head in amazement.

'To be honest, it was all in a day's work. I pity the poor blokes in the trenches.'

WEDNESDAY, 30TH OCTOBER 1918

'Listen to this, Ada,' Ernie yelled at his wife who was on the other side of the kitchen. *'Turkey signs Armistice with Allies. Marks defeat of the Ottoman Empire, Germany's main Ally.'*

Ada came over to her husband and read the newspaper headline over his shoulder.

'Maybe this means the blooming war will finally end. Can't come soon enough.'

Hers was a voice you could have heard in every household throughout the land. War weariness combined with shortages of almost everything was sapping the nation's confidence and resilience.

'Fred was one of the lucky ones then,' Ernie said thankfully. His brother had suffered a gunshot wound to the right arm during the Gallipoli campaign and had been evacuated on the hospital ship, SS *France*, to a US base hospital near Bordeaux. It had been mid-1916 before they'd received a letter from him telling how he was being well looked after by some wonderful nurses from Massachusetts whom the patients had named 'the Bordeaux belles'. At least, now, with Turkey out of the war there was a chance it might all be over in Europe soon too, they both thought.

'I pity the poor blokes in the trenches' – Ernie hadn't been able to get those words uttered by the young Merchant Navy cadet out of his mind. It was now eighteen months since John

Pridmore had been killed in action at Vimy Ridge and yet the war on the Western Front had ground on, consuming lives at an alarming rate. In April 1918 British and French forces had been pushed back by a massive German spring offensive – heavily reinforced by troops returning from the Eastern Front following Russia's withdrawal from the war. In May, the Allies, with the help of General Pershing's American Expeditionary Force, had checked the German advance. At last it felt like the tide was turning against the Kaiser's army and people at home started believing an end to the war was in sight. But that optimism was premature. Heavy fighting continued throughout the summer with casualties mounting on both sides. *The war to end all wars*, as the popular press was describing it, still seemed a long way off.

Then around the middle of the year, soldiers on both sides of the conflict started to fall sick to a deadly strain of influenza. No one could believe it at first, but by the autumn, losses due to it were exceeding combat casualties, especially amongst the weakened German Army. Spain – a neutral country during the war, with an uncensored press – had reported cases of *La Grippe* as early as May. The English-speaking press coined it *the Spanish flu* and soon it was wreaking havoc around the world.

The first wave of the pandemic was relatively mild, causing symptoms such as headaches, sore throats and loss of appetite. Although highly infectious in the cramped trenches, soldiers recovered. But then a second, highly contagious wave appeared, turning the skin of its victims' blue and filling the lungs with fluid that led to suffocation. Sufferers, young adults in particular, died of pneumonia within hours of developing symptoms. The illness continued to spread like wildfire, affecting civilians as well as soldiers.

MONDAY, 11ᵀᴴ NOVEMBER 1918

News of the ceasefire on the Western Front flashed up from the Nore sandbank on the Estuary, officially reaching Gravesend's Terrace Pier some six hours after the Armistice was signed. On the eleventh hour, of the eleventh day, of the eleventh month of 1918, the guns finally fell silent.

Every skipper on every tug, boat and ship on the Thames sounded their horns. Ernie and his crew threw their caps in the air, waving frantically at the growing crowd already collecting on the prom.

As soon as she heard the commotion, Ada grabbed toddler Ernie and ran next door to her parents' house. For the first time in four and a half years she knew they were safe. The morning newspaper had said it was almost certain that the guns on the Front would fall silent today.

'Let's have a bit of a party later,' suggested Ada after the family had all hugged and kissed one another. 'If we club all our coupons together, I can make a cake and we'll be ready to start when Ern gets home from work.'

'Oh, I've got a blue one left,' said Mrs Stone, appearing from the kitchen waving her ration book. 'We can have bread and scrape, and there's always them tomatoes I bottled in salt which have never been opened.'

No one had tasted any more than a few grains of sugar in their tea since January and by April, meat, butter and cheese had been rationed too. It took a while for everyone to get used to the different-coloured coupons, but it cut down on the queues, and the country still had enough food despite the three thousand or more British merchant ships and fishing boats having been sunk. Ernie's newspaper produced a weekly supplement giving recipes and tips on preserving, which Ada and her mother had tried, much to the consternation of their husbands, but it all helped and no one truly starved.

Coal shortages had meant that shops and pubs were only allowed to be open a few hours and since the days had got shorter, everyone went to bed earlier. Unsurprisingly, the pubs were packed to bursting for the hours they were allowed to be open on this momentous day. Union Jacks appeared in shop windows and everyone in Bernard Street had them draped over their front doors or waving in the wind from upstairs windows. Large crowds started piling out into the High Street and complete strangers joined arms and sang and danced, overwhelmed with joy and relief.

Hilda and Mabel were delighted when word of a procession, from the Town Hall to the Clock Tower, reached their ears. Hastily dressed up as Land Girls, they ran to join in. Young Ernie waved his little flag furiously when he saw them coming towards him, each laughing as they tripped over wearing their father's Wellington boots.

By the time Ernie Senior had finished work and joined them, murky grey November clouds had formed so they returned home to start their own party. It didn't take long before a dozen neighbours were crammed round the new upright grand piano in the parlour of number 10, laughter mixing with tears for most of the night.

MONDAY, 25TH NOVEMBER 1918

George held his mother's mirror so that Ernie could sort out his collar and tie. With starch unavailable for laundering purposes, no amount of adjusting would make his limp collar look smart.

'That'll do,' said George. 'It's as good as it's gunna get. Besides, I can't 'old this blessed thing much longer. I've only got one good arm and I bet I'll be doing it again in a minute so Ma can get 'er titfa on straight.' Both men laughed, Ernie offering to oblige when they heard Nance call for help.

'Been a while since you were sharing my bedroom, Ern. I'm only sorry it's for such a sad reason.'

'I know,' agreed Ernie. 'I can't believe I'm going to our baby Ada's funeral. She was only sixteen and it's terrible to think she died all alone in the infirmary.'

'It all 'appened so fast – no one could get there in time,' consoled George. 'But at least she knew she 'ad a brother who cared.'

'I'd just managed to persuade 'er to come down to Gravesend and meet young Ern for the first time.'

'You've done a good job with the other girls too. Lily comes often and even Betsy's been 'ere for tea. Ma was ever so pleased.'

Eventually, after a full-scale search for her black gloves, Nance was ready. Leaving her son in charge of the shop, she and Ernie set off for Canning Town and for the best funeral they could afford for young Ada.

'Evil, this flu,' whispered Nance after sitting on the train in silence for a while. 'As if our young men and women 'aven't suffered enough.'

Ernie had found out about his sister's death on, of all days, 12th November. Everyone had been up half the night celebrating the Armistice and his head was banging as hard as the door knocker. Unable to eat any breakfast, he struggled to focus on the blunt telegram message written in pencil: *Ada passed away. Come at once. Aunt Polly.*

By late afternoon, he was heading for Canning Town trying to fathom out what could have happened. He hadn't heard his sister was ill, let alone at death's door. It never entered his head that she might fall prey to the flu that the troops returning from the Front were bringing with them. Nor could he have known that the airborne virus would become a global pandemic killing fifty million people worldwide.

'It's shocking, Ern, all over so quick. I went as soon as I got word she wasn't well and only stopped at Popkins on the 'ermit Road to get 'er a nice bit of fish,' Polly said as she gave him a cup of reviving tea and a couple of aspirins. 'But when I got there, she'd already gone to the infirmary. The cook said she was coughing a bit yesterday but enjoyed the celebrations. During the night, though, 'er lips turned blue and she started struggling for air. They called an ambulance.' Ernie wrapped his arms around his aunt as she burst into tears and it was quite a while before she was able to speak again. 'She died of that Spanish flu, right after the war was over. Oh, Ernie, what a sad little life she 'ad.'

Polly, Nance and Ernie were the first to arrive at St Luke's Church. It was freezing, so the warden let them wait inside.

'Last time I was in 'ere was for Sam's funeral,' Nance said wistfully. 'Seems a lot longer than six years ago. Course, all us sisters got married in 'ere too and 'ad our children churched and baptised in that font. I suppose every family from the Tidal

Basin will say the same about this church. It's seen us all come and go. I'm glad you chose it for Ada, Ern, it's only right.'

Choked, Ernie was relieved when the double doors opened, and he saw his cousins Daisy and Mary arm and arm.

'Thank 'eavens you've arrived,' said their mother. 'We've been 'aving a trip down memory lane. Made us quite tearful already.'

'Good job we've got some spare 'ankies then,' responded Daisy. 'Reckon we're gunna need 'em. I'm not sure anyone else will be 'ere, so that's sad in itself.'

'Oh, I think Lily will come,' said Nance.

'And maybe even Betsy,' chipped in Ernie, looking at his pocket watch. 'Ladies, it's time we were outside, the 'earse will be arriving any minute.'

Ernie sat through the short service holding his sister Betsy's hand. He had been shocked to see her shivering outside in a thin, shabby coat not suitable for the November weather. At only eighteen, she looked worryingly pale – already faded by hard toil. So concerned had he been, and so delighted to see Lily there too, that he hadn't notice a third woman standing by the gravestones. It was only when he heard sobbing during the prayers and turned to look towards the back pews that he realised who she was.

'Who is that woman?' Betsy asked with a look of surprise on her face.

Ernie's could feel the hair standing up on the back of his neck. 'It's our mother,' he said quietly.

Everyone held it together until they were back outside. Nance and Polly were furious that Sarah had turned up without warning. She may have been their sister, but they hadn't seen her in nearly fifteen years and all this wailing and crying about 'losing her baby' just didn't cut any ice with them.

''Ow dare you do this?' Ernie snapped at her. 'Crying over *your baby*. That's all Ada was when you disappeared, and you've not been back since. Where were you when Bill got drowned?'

By this time Sarah had torn herself away from her sisters and was now throwing herself at her daughters, begging for forgiveness and telling them she wanted to be part of their lives again. Daisy went to Ernie's side and Mary to Betsy's, who was now sobbing. Lily was trying her best not to show any emotion and looked like she was ready to make a bolt for it.

Daisy could see the girls needed rescuing. 'Let's go back to my 'ouse,' she said, comforting them. 'Let it all sink in.'

'She could 'ave been dead and buried 'erself, for all we knew,' Ernie spat, red with rage as he turned to walk away before saying something he'd regret.

The siblings would all need time to sort out their emotions and for each one to decide whether they were prepared to let their mother back into their lives. Ernie had no intention of doing so. He'd always had the love and support of his aunts. The others had been given no such love in the institution. They'd been separated, alone and with little or no memory of having parents, brothers and sisters. Until he'd heard the full story from his brother, Joe believed himself to be an orphan.

Ernie had worked hard to get Fred, Harry, Joe, Lily, Betsy and Ada to realise they were part of a family and not six 'only' children. Earning their trust had been easier with some than others. But he knew it was what Bill would have done had he not lost his life on the *Britannia* ten years ago. That baton had passed to Ernie and he was determined to succeed no matter how long it took, or what obstacles he needed to overcome along the way.

MONDAY, 10ᵀᴴ JANUARY 1927

'Are you ready, Ern? You're due to be meeting 'er soon,' Nance shouted up the stairs.

Ernie felt terrible; he'd been up half the night thinking about what he was going to say when he saw his mother again for the first time since his sister's funeral and he'd hardly given her a thought during all that time. Raking over the past wasn't something he did, but the mess-up over his brother's birth certificate had brought it all back again.

'All you've got to do is get my sister to sign the declaration and it will be sorted,' his aunt said, straightening his tie just like she always had.

Ernie went to give her a peck on the cheek which set Jack's parrot off and chaos ensued. Unable to resist tormenting the squawking bird, feathers flew everywhere. 'Go on, get out of 'ere!' Nance laughed as she pushed him out of the shop with her broom.

Closing the door behind him, Ernie gritted his teeth against the cold. Totting up the years on his fingers, he realised that it had been nearly three since Nance had got married again. Everyone liked Jack Allen and his parrot. He was a kindly man and a good companion, but the shop still had the name Pridmore outside. 'And that's 'ow it will stay,' Nance said firmly when anyone asked.

Looking around, it was comforting to see that not much else had changed in Cyprus Place either. Women were still proudly scrubbing their front steps despite the rats running across the roads and the Ferndale appeared to be full of weary dock and gas workers with little to say. Crossing Shepstone Street, he waved at George and wife Harriet now running their own grocers at number 11, on the corner.

Tidal Basin, on the other hand, looked and felt very different. It still carried the scars of the previous year's disaster, when the Thames and the dock overflowed. People had to stay upstairs until the water receded and the stench was vile. But there was far more to it than that: Crown Street, Catherine Street and the Victoria Dock Road had got the nickname 'Draughtboard Alley' after Caribbean, African and Asian seamen and ex-servicemen had settled in West Ham, mixing in with the local population after the War. The welcome they received could hardly have been called friendly and the newly opened Coloured Men's Institute on Tidal Basin Road was the only safe haven they felt they had.

The Irish weren't made to feel welcome either – which annoyed Nance and her sisters. 'West 'am was 'appy enough for us to build its railways and dig its docks,' she often said, 'yet they still treat us like dirt.' It was a sore point amongst local Catholic families. Old antagonisms die hard. When the Church of St Vincent de Paul on Stratford High Street had been built, there were no windows on the front for fear of them being smashed by anti-Irish rioters.

Times had always been hard, but as Ernie looked around, they seemed even worse now. He was shocked to see the streets full of children displaying signs of malnutrition and women queuing at the pawn shops with their freshly washed bedding parcelled up ready to be left till payday. At the end of the war, Prime Minister Lloyd George had promised 'a land fit for heroes', yet demobilised servicemen hadn't been able to find work. Unemployment was now at an all-time high, deprivation widespread and industrial relations in tatters. The 1926 General Strike had lasted only nine days after coal mine owners locked striking miners out of the pits. Ernie had watched a dozen dockers place themselves around the sides of a lorry and then tip it over, whether it was full of cargo or not. There were scores and scores of overturned lorries lining each side of the East India Dock Road during that time.

War debts had brought heavy cuts in education, public health and workers' benefits. The West Ham Board of Guardians owed the Government nearly two million pounds which it had borrowed to pay poor relief, so the Ministry of Health had taken over the board's affairs, cutting relief payments even further. Surely it can't get much worse, Ernie thought to himself as he crossed Stratford Broadway before shielding himself from the wind behind one of the Town Hall's impressive pillars.

Turning his thoughts to his youngest brother, Ernie's mood lightened a little. Despite being on the other side of the world, Joe was the sibling he felt closest to and now that he wanted to marry, getting his name and date of birth officially corrected, would be a great relief.

It was back in April 1922 when Joe wrote to his brother from his ship HMS *Cricket* enquiring about work in London. Ernie had replied advising him that his job prospects were low and, as a single man, he should stay and find work in the Far East. Receiving a free discharge from the Navy and with a good reference from his commanding officer, Joe joined the Shanghai Municipal Police Force.

Shanghai was a city of two parts. The International Settlement had grown rapidly since 1843 when the Chinese government agreed to concede land outside the city walls to the British as a trading post. Joined by the Americans and French later, the Settlement existed as a separate entity from Chinese Shanghai, with its own governing body and a British-style police force with a headquarters and fourteen local stations.

At the time Joe became a policeman, the seven thousand British residents within the Settlement were made up of a wealthy expatriate elite and a large settler community. This latter group referred to themselves as Shanghailanders and included the police force. They had a distinct identity with their own social practices and rules. Learning Chinese was seen as demeaning and mixing with the indigenous community was frowned upon. With very few single British women there, many of the policemen remained unmarried during their time in Shanghai. However, there was a source of single female companions in the shape of governesses, interpreters and hospital nurses of different nationalities. Joe had reached thirty before he met Juanita Elisa Greiner and asked her to marry him.

'You look like you're doing alright for yourself,' Sarah declared after she and Ernie had finished their business at the Town Hall. 'Captain now, I 'ear. I always knew you were the one who'd go far.'

Ernie bit his tongue, buttoned up his donkey jacket and turned towards the station.

'Surely you can spare the time to buy your old ma a cup of tea and tell 'er all your news,' she said, grabbing at his sleeve. 'I need to wet me whistle before I go back to Spitalfields.'

Begrudgingly Ernie led the way into the nearest café, where, while waiting for his order, he studied his mother's reflection in the mirror behind the counter. With her lank, greying hair and a badly lined face, she bore little resemblance to the woman he remembered as a child. Despite appearing tough on the outside, the sadness in her eyes betrayed her inner vulnerability. It reminded him of Polly. Since Jim's death, her eyes looked like that too.

'I know,' she said cheeringly and breaking the silence that had engulfed her son, 'I'll tell you what Poll's told me about you and your family and then you can add the rest.'

It turned out there wasn't much she didn't know. Ernie and Ada had had a second child in 1920, a girl they named Iris. Young Ernie had recently caught diphtheria and spent several weeks in an isolation hospital, his parents only able to see him through a window. Ernie had been a tug skipper on the *Sirdar* for the past four years. He still played football for teams in Gravesend and Northfleet, and he'd won rowing races at Putney and got medals to prove it.

He kept in contact with Fred but didn't see him much as he had his own family. Harry and Lily he saw even less of, but thanks to Ada's efforts, Betsy now spent her holidays with them.

As for herself, she had a nice little room in a tenement, just off Commercial Street. She'd slaved for Abraham Goldman in his tobacconists for years but couldn't carry on like that no more. Rheumatism had put paid to that. She got by these days doing laundry for the local doss houses. The area was full of foreigners – refugees from the Balkans who came over after the war, Lithuanians, Czechoslovakians, Albanians, Romanians and lord knows who else. She didn't much care for their butchers selling horseflesh, but their queer-shaped bread smelt good. She had hopes of settling down one day with the caretaker of her building. He'd talked of them moving to Islington when he retired, and she still wished with all her heart that her children would let her back into their lives. Oh, and she was still in touch with her sister-in-law Eliza, who had never been lucky in life. Turns out her Charlie, whom she'd married in 1917, died of his war wounds two years later, but not before giving her another child on top of the one she'd been carrying when they married. Luckily her father, old Henry, who died the same year, left her a bit in his will. At least that kept them going until her eldest was old enough to go out to work.

'I 'ear Joe's going to bring 'is new wife back, for you all to meet,' Sarah said at the end of her monologue, aware that Ernie was itching to go their separate ways.

'They're coming in May on the *Devanha* and staying with Ada and me for three months,' he confirmed, lighting a cigarette as he got up from his seat.

'I'll be praying that 'e'll want to see 'is ma,' she responded rather pathetically.

Ernie gave her a long hard look before leaving the café and heading for the station. From the correspondence he and his brother had exchanged over the years that seemed unlikely. Joe believed that it was because of her that he had suffered at the hands of the do-gooders who'd sent him to a Nautical School for the Destitute. Training, as far as he was concerned, was about moulding children like him into 'material for the services', robbing them of individual character and forcing them to endure frequent punishment.

Ernie remembered watching a procession of these 'Charity Children' when he himself could so easily have become one. He had cowered in a shop doorway as they marched past like prisoners. With little appetite for laughter, they looked more like little old men and women than children. 'As cold as charity' was a phrase only the poor truly understood.

On the journey home, he wondered if Joe, or any of them for that matter, would have fared better remaining with a neglectful mother and a sick father rather than enduring the discipline, loneliness and uncaring routines of an institution? Even the most dishevelled hovel and the most careless of parents offered some kind of personal contact. And even if life had been explosive, as theirs often was, at least they would have had the comfort of being in it all together.

Ernie just thanked his lucky stars he had managed to get away and make a different kind of life for himself. But he'd never forgotten that it was his experiences growing up here, that had moulded him into the man he'd become.

SUNDAY, 29TH AUGUST 1937

Ernie and his daughter Iris were in the back yard sorting out his tools and old tobacco tins full of screws and nails. The family were about to move to 42 Brandon Street and Ada had made it clear that, although it was a bigger house, she didn't want all her husband's junk moving with them.

Hearing the back gate opening, Iris poked her head out of the coal bunker to see her brother making his way up the path. 'You're back early, everything alright?' she asked, picking cobwebs out of her hair.

'Bit of a disastrous date,' young Ernie said, looking somewhat flustered. 'In fact I couldn't get the train back from Chatham quick enough. When I got to the house, she wanted me to meet her dad. Got the shock of me life when I went in the room. There he was, looking at himself in the mirror. He's a *Blackshirt*, Sis. Everything he was wearing was black except for a great big silver belt buckle which had been polished till it was gleaming. When he saw me, he raised his right arm in the fascist salute. Sent shivers down my spine, I can tell you.'

'I thought they couldn't wear that stuff no more. Not since what 'appened in Cable Street.'

'S'pose that's why he can only prance around in his kitchen,' her brother replied, demonstrating what he meant. 'But that's only the half of it. She suggested we went for a walk and blow me down if I don't see him again. We've ended up in Batchelor

Street and there's a thousand people chanting, "Mind Britain's Business!" They're all wearing red, white and blue armbands now and saluting to the National Anthem. Did have to laugh, though, her dad's got the most important job. He has to stand guard in case someone tries to cut the wires to their loudspeaker. Happens often, I gather.'

'That Oswald Mosley's been shouting the odds all over Medway. 'E was in Rochester not that long ago,' Ernie said, raising his eyebrows as he emerged from the shed. 'Stopped all the traffic in Corporation Street. I can remember going to 'ear 'im and Ernest Bevan speak in Gravesend. Course they was both Labour politicians at that time. 'E's certainly changed 'is tune since then. I ain't bought the *Daily Mail* since.'

Going inside for a cup of tea, Ernie Senior told his son a bit more about Mosley and his crowd. 'Nineteen twenty-nine it was, the year Labour won the election and the first time all women could vote like the men. My cousin Daisy wasn't likely to let me forget *that*.' He laughed. 'Actually she wrote to me after she saw Mosley spouting 'is views in Stratford Town 'all. It seems a lot of women are joining the fascists so she went to see what all the fuss was about. Apparently every time some brave soul interrupted, dozens of Blackshirts pounced on 'em. It was brutal. Aunt Nance went to 'ear 'im too, in East 'am and it was much the same. West 'am stopped letting them use their premises after that, so now they're on Wanstead Flats every Sunday afternoon causing trouble.'

In 1931, disillusioned with British politics, Oswald Mosley went on a study tour of the 'new movements' of Italy's Benito Mussolini. Convinced that it was the way forward for Britain, he formed the British Union of Fascists a year later. When the meetings started being disrupted, he instituted a corps of black-uniformed paramilitary stewards, the Fascist Defence Force, nicknamed the 'Blackshirts'.

Newspaper proprietor Lord Rothermere gave his full support to the BUF, writing in the *Daily Mail* on 22nd January 1934:

*'Hurrah for the Blackshirts. Timid alarmists all this
week have been whimpering that the rapid growth in
numbers of the British Blackshirts is preparing the way
for a system of rulership by means of steel whips and
concentration camps. Very few of these panic-mongers
have any personal knowledge of the countries that are
already under Blackshirt government. The notion that a
permanent reign of terror exists there has been evolved
entirely from their own morbid imaginations, fed by
sensational propaganda from opponents of the party
now in power. As a purely British organisation, the
Blackshirts will respect those principals of tolerance which
are traditional in British politics. They have no prejudice
either of class or race.'*

Contrary to this belief, within a year, Mosley was making
violent anti-Semitic speeches which received praise from Adolf
Hitler. Deciding on a strategy to campaign in Jewish areas, he
announced that his British Union of Fascists intended to march
through the East End on 4th October 1936.

Of the three hundred and fifty thousand Jews living in
Britain, about one hundred and fifty thousand were in the East
End of London, sixty thousand of them in Stepney alone. Within
forty-eight hours more than seventy-seven thousand local
people had signed a petition asking for the event to be banned
by the Government. Not wanting to infringe freedom of speech,
the Home Secretary instead sent a police escort to prevent anti-
fascist protestors from disrupting the march.

Adopting the slogan of the Spanish Republicans ¡No
pasarán! – *They Shall Not Pass* – banners and barricades were
erected across Cable Street in Stepney and fifty thousand
working-class people gathered behind them. As the police
tried to clear a route for the Blackshirts by making repeated
baton charges, demonstrators fought back with sticks and
chair legs. The contents of chamber pots and rotten vegetables
were thrown by the wives of Irish dockers from their upstairs

windows. Eventually the Commissioner of the Metropolitan Police accepted defeat and told Mosley to abandon the march through Cable Street.

The 1936 Public Order Act, brought in soon after, gave the Home Secretary the power to ban marches, the wearing of political uniforms and the use of threatening and abusive words.

'Daisy says that now the BUF have become more respectable, they are drumming up quite a bit of support in West 'am,' Ernie added, finishing off the conversation. 'Upton and Forest Gate mainly, but they're getting a good audience at Beckton Road in Canning Town.'

FRIDAY, 31ˢᵗ DECEMBER 1937

'Will it seem strange not going back to Shanghai?' Ada asked her sister-in-law.

Nita nodded as she crammed the freshly made sausage rolls in the oven. 'Life is so different there. The Bund is packed with banks and businesses and people have money to spend in the casinos and at the racetrack.'

The more Ada heard about the nightclubs, ballrooms and the Nanking Road lined with restaurants, hotels and department stores, the more she realised that Nita's life in the International Settlement couldn't have been more different from hers. They had lived in an upstairs apartment, travelled around in a rickshaw and their children were used to having a Chinese nursemaid called an amah. With Joe having risen up the police force ranks to sub-inspector, there was no doubt that their lives in Shanghai had been better than he could ever have achieved in a Britain experiencing the continuing effects of the Depression. The high life had taken its toll on some of Joe's colleagues, though. Drinking and gambling led to them running up huge debts, but that was nothing compared to the perils of drug taking in the opium dens.

'Let's have another look at that picture, Ern,' Joe said, putting the last washed glass on the draining board and drying his hands on the tea towel.

Buried amongst Ada's knitting patterns in the sideboard drawer, Ernie found a sepia photograph and handed it to his brother.

'So that's our mother, is it? I can hardly make out what it says on the back for all the kisses she's covered it in. Taken after their wedding, you reckon. Well, he's wearing a collar and tie, so that's something, I suppose.'

At sixty-two, Sarah Pridmore remarried and the pair had retired to Islington. Joe hadn't seen her since he was a small child, so there wasn't much else to say on the matter.

'Right, you lot,' Ernie declared decisively after throwing the photo back from whence it came, 'we need to tap that barrel and get this party going.'

Alerted to the sound of Ernie tuning the piano, friends and neighbours were soon piling in. Presented with a ukulele, Joe rushed upstairs and returned wearing his wife's Chinese Dragon dressing gown. Donning the traditional coolie hat and fan they'd brought back as presents, he looked the very spit of George Formby's Mr Wu. Everyone fell about in stitches as he belted out 'Chinese Laundry Blues' – the most popular song of the day – accompanied by young Ernie on his mother's washboard.

Ada, Betsy and Iris kept the sausage rolls and pickled onions coming, and the celebrations continued until the last dregs of beer finally ran out well into the New Year.

Ernie tossed and turned that night. He'd definitely had too much to drink, but there was more than that keeping him awake. The world was in turmoil again. Following the abdication of Edward VIII, Britain now had a new King who no one was sure was up to the job. Prime Minister Neville Chamberlain seemed willing to placate rather than confront an increasingly aggressive Germany. Hitler was openly aiding the nationalist General Francisco Franco in a savage civil war designed to bring down the democratically elected Republican Government in Madrid. Spanish towns were being bombed indiscriminately by the Luftwaffe, revealing the frightening prospect of a future air war against any country prepared to stand up to the Nazis. Japan had invaded China, occupying Peking, and was now surrounding Shanghai. 'Thank God Joe and Nita are finally back in England for good,' he mistakenly said out loud. Ada stirred but didn't wake. Not wanting to disturb her, he went downstairs to his favourite fireside chair.

The closer the Japanese had got to Shanghai, the clearer it became that SMP members and their families needed to be evacuated. With a typhoon raging on the day they left, Joe, Nita, their three young children and all their belongings were forced to stay in temporary accommodation on shore until it calmed. Joe told his brother that as they finally boarded ship he could hear the sound of fighting on the other side of the city. Arriving at Southampton, six weeks later, it had been decided that the family would temporarily live in Cyprus Place. The children moved into the shop with Aunt Nance and Jack, with Joe and Nita at George and Harriet's shop a few doors down. Ernie had to smile at the thought of Cyprus-on-Thames coming to the rescue again.

There was no doubt another war was coming. Gravesend was already making preparations to protect the public in the event of an air raid. Men were being asked to volunteer for work as Air Raid Wardens. An experimental air raid had already taken place. Ernie had been scared to light a cigarette in the kitchen during the blackout for fear of being spotted by the wardens.

Watching the sun slowly rising he knew only too well that it was the fate of young Ernie that was the cause of his lack of sleep. The boy was soon to celebrate being twenty-one and was currently a lighterman in his last year as an apprentice. If war came, who knows where he'd be posted. Maybe he'd be in a reserved occupation, but there was no guarantee of that.

Warfare was going to be very different this time and maybe even more awful than 1914–18. Having finally achieved a sense of peace in his own journey through life, the thought of his son being in danger was just too much to contemplate.

WEDNESDAY, 11TH SEPTEMBER 1940

'Ernie… what the devil's happened to your hair?'

No sooner had she said it Ada realised how stupid it sounded. Abandoning the cooking apples, half sliced, she rushed to the back door and threw her arms around her husband's neck.

'I thought you were a gonner,' she whispered through her tears, the smell of fire and burning filling her nostrils.

'So did I, girl,' he whispered back, holding on to her tightly. 'Now put that bloody knife down. I ain't dodged all them bombs only to 'ave me jugular cut by me own wife.' Dropping the knife in the scullery sink, they both laughed, but Ada could feel him shaking.

'I've got to sit down, legs won't 'old up much longer. Not 'ad a wink of sleep for four nights.'

Supporting the man she had loved for twenty-five years, Ada guided him into the kitchen. Taking his cap off and placing it on the table, Ernie all but collapsed into his favourite armchair. His face was extremely sore, but he was too tired to attend to it now. As he closed his eyes, he could still see the blazing orange and red sky.

Watching him drift off to sleep, Ada was shocked at his sorry appearance. Where his cap had covered his head, he still had most of his thick, greying hair, but the bits round his ears had been burnt off and he no longer had any eyebrows. His face was red-raw and peeling, and his lips were blistered. As for his uniform, there wasn't much that could be done with it. Those brass buttons won't ever be shiny again, she thought as she reached for the Zam-Buk ointment. Still, the PLA can sort that out. It's the least they can do seeing as how he's been out fighting fires for them.

She'd been worrying since the Thursday before when the oil storage tanks at Thameshaven were attacked, the fires lighting up the sky for hours. The London docks were an obvious target and that made her husband a target too.

Putting the apples into a saucepan, with a spoonful of the week's precious sugar ration, Ada quietly placed it on the stove to stew later. Filling the kettle, she looked back at Ernie and wondered what lay ahead for them now the country was well and truly at war again. 'Better be all over before Iris's wedding next April,' she whispered. 'Can't have young Ern stuck out at sea either, seeing as he's best man.'

THURSDAY, 12ᵀᴴ SEPTEMBER 1940

'Ernie, Ernie, wake up...' Ada was shaking her husband's arm. 'Churchill's on the wireless in a minute.'

'What, 'ow long 'ave I been asleep?' He looked around with a dazed expression.

'Quite a while and you've been calling out a lot.'

She could tell he was disorientated and it worried her to see how tired he still looked. As she bent over to kiss him, tiny black flecks of coal dust in the creases on his face glinted in the daylight.

Sitting at the kitchen table, they listened to the Prime Minister's address:

> 'We cannot tell when they will try to come; we cannot be sure that in fact they will try at all; but no one should blind himself to the fact that a heavy, full-scale invasion of this island is being prepared with all the usual German thoroughness and method, and that it may be launched now – upon England, upon Scotland, or upon Ireland, or upon all three... Every man and woman will therefore prepare himself to do his duty, whatever it may be, with special pride and care.'

'That can't be right,' Ada declared, too stunned to take it all in. 'Makes no sense.'

'It would if you'd seen what I've seen, love. The docks are all ablaze and 'itler ain't finished with us yet.'

At the outbreak of the Second World War, in September 1939, no one really knew what to expect and lived through a wet, cold winter in anxious anticipation of bombers arriving over British cities. Barrage balloons appeared in the sky and sandbags were piled round the entrances to shops and public buildings. It was thought that the Germans would use chemical weapons on civilian populations and so some forty million gas masks were issued. Having been told to carry them everywhere, Iris and her best friend stowed them under their seats at the Majestic on a night out to see the Billy Cotton Bandshow and then had to go running back when they realised they'd come out without them. When white lines and dashes were painted along the middle of Gravesend's roads to aid motorists in the blackout, it caused quite a stir. No one in Brandon Street had a car, but quite a large crowd gathered to watch it being done nevertheless.

When little or nothing had happened by early summer 1940, the newspapers started calling it the *phoney war*. Many of the evacuated children began to return and people regretted the seven hundred and fifty thousand household pets they'd had put down. Even the barrage balloons were beginning to be a nuisance, either bursting into flames in thunderstorms or breaking away in high winds, their wires trailing across roofs and damaging chimney pots. Then, on that glorious sunny September afternoon, the sirens sounded in earnest. Like many others living along the Thames estuary, Ada had first heard a dull droning and came outside to watch black specks, like a swarm of flies, filling the sky. When clouds of thick black smoke appeared, she knew the first bombs were falling on London.

Even though Ernie had been off duty for twenty-four hours, the screaming of the bombs falling out of the sky and the *whump* of the explosions still haunted him. His chest hurt from the suction and compression of high explosives and his eyes were still watering from the clouds of acrid smoke pouring from burning rubber, chemical and paint factories. He could remember every detail – from the very first wave of incendiaries that set fire to the wood sheds at five p.m. on that Saturday; how he and his crew went ashore and formed a human chain to pass buckets of water while the hoses were being connected; how he manoeuvred the *Sirdar* as close as he dared, holding the tug steady whilst his men took turns to direct water onto the seat of the fires until they were extinguished, then spraying each other to cool down.

The next night had been far worse. The still-burning woodsheds along the curve of the river circling the Isle of Dogs made West India Dock an easy target for the bomb-aimers. From nine p.m. the *Sirdar* towed craft and their merchandise away from the quayside to places of safety. At midnight orders were received to proceed to the blazing Rum Quay, where the Belgian merchant ship SS *Indier* was in danger of being set alight.

Ernie felt a cold shiver up his spine as he re-lived the hours that followed. West India Dock was full of produce from the Empire. The air was loaded with burning pepper which hurt like hell when it got into his eyes and lungs. As he took on a towrope from the bows of the *Indier*, rum barrels exploded around him, setting the water on fire, and shards of lethal shrapnel dropped like rain, tearing anything they encountered to ribbons. What amazed him was how deftly they'd managed to move the ship clear of blazing barges. When, at two forty-five, a high explosive bomb struck the middle of number 13 Shed sending thousands of vats of rum sky high, the rush of air across the dock sent the *Sirdar* spinning.

Somehow, he and his crew had survived it all.

Ernest Pridmore, Master of Tug

FRIDAY, 13TH SEPTEMBER 1940

'They're calling the 7th *Black Saturday*,' Ada said, not sure that her husband could hear her from the bathroom. 'According to this, *four hundred and fifty lost their lives*. Looks like forty of them were killed in one air-raid shelter alone. Winston went to Shoreditch to see it for himself on Sunday. He had to clamber over the wreckage.'

Putting the copy of the *Daily Mirror* on the table, she poked her head round the bathroom door. 'Do you *have* to go back so soon?'

Of course, she knew the answer to that question. Ernie was already having a shave, his uniform, which she'd done her best to clean, waiting on its hanger. He had to be back on the *Sirdar* to carry out his shift, regardless of how he felt.

Thousands of bombs and incendiary devices had been dropped since that first night, many strapped to oil drums to aid the conflagration. Silvertown – home to the most highly flammable materials – had come off particularly badly, its rubber works still burning fiercely. Now he was going to have to make his way back there to join his exhausted crew.

Despite many railway lines being out of action, Ernie was able to buy his workman's ticket to Woolwich Arsenal as usual and joined a platform full of people all wondering what they would find when the train arrived in London. Parts of the Thames shoreline were still ablaze – warehouses, wharves, piers and barges. On hearing that the Greenwich Foot Tunnel had been penetrated by a bomb falling at low tide, he hoped that the Woolwich Tunnel, which took him to the George V dock, hadn't been hit as well.

'Still in one piece... so far, anyway,' said the tunnel's lift operator, seeing the tug skipper approaching. 'Mind where you walk down there. They've been mopping it out since the all-clear went, but it's a devil of a job keeping it clean with the hundreds that's been packed in there at night. ARP men supposed to stop them coming, but there's too many. Point is, they don't stand a chance if a bomb drops in the river overhead.'

With a full load, he closed the gates and took them down. Ten feet below the riverbed, the familiar damp air enveloped Ernie as he started to walk the half mile under the river. As a young man, he had watched the navvies digging the tunnel out by hand and had been at the grand opening in 1912 when on the crew of the tug *Dunera*. Stepping over piles of rubbish and forgotten blankets he wondered what all the posh women in their finery, who had made the journey on that day, would make of it being used as a bomb shelter.

Thinking back even further, he remembered when he and his older brother Bill would muck about in the old Greenwich tunnel. Running as fast as they could from one side to the other, they'd bounce off the ceramic tiles until either hurting themselves or getting shouted at. It made him smile.

Flicking up the collar of his donkey jacket, Ernie looked at his watch and picked up speed. He had deliberately left home early as he wanted to make sure Polly and Nance had survived the weekend and were prepared for what was still to come. Then he would head to work, no doubt just in time for the siren to go off again. It was obvious from what he'd seen and heard that the area around the Royal Victoria and Albert Docks had been hit hard, so he was expecting the worst when he emerged from the other end of the tunnel in North Woolwich. Being brought up in the poorest parts of East and West Ham, life was always about expecting the worst, he thought.

'Lift's not working this end, and the station canopy's collapsed on the trains,' someone shouted from up above. 'I'd put a handkerchief over your nose and mouth as you come up the stairs. The smoke will hit you first. There's not much left up here, believe me.'

Despite the warning, Ernie was ill-prepared for the devastation that greeted him. The grain refinery he had seen on fire had now collapsed into the river, and boats were taking people, carrying whatever they had left in the world, off the pier.

It was déjà vu. He'd experienced Silvertown in a similar state during the Great War. Realising that getting to Canning Town was going to be a challenge, he started walking along Albert Road towards the station, though he didn't hold out much hope of the trains running. Luckily a man driving a London taxi that had been converted into a makeshift fire engine, complete with ladder and sand buckets, stopped when he spotted Ernie's uniform and offered to take him as far as the Connaught Bridge.

'You should 'ave seen it on Saturday night,' he said, offering Ernie a cigarette while zigzagging round fallen masonry. 'Tate and Lyle and the rubber works got 'it badly, but Pinchin & Johnson's factory was the worst. Paint tins turned into mortars. Well, that and the tar distillery. Bloody stuff was oozing across the road like lava.' Ernie nodded, not inclined to share his own experiences.

Pleased to see Cundy's pub was still standing despite having had all its windows blown out, Ernie thanked his driver and made his way along the Victoria Dock Road. At the Hack Road end of Catherine Street and where he and Bill had been born, a high explosive dropped on Black Saturday had done extensive damage. Two more had landed in the street later that night. Numbers 22, 24 and 26 were gone and rescue workers were clawing at the rubble in a desperate bid to find anyone still alive. Blankets lay amongst the debris covering body parts. It seemed unreal. Then, out of the blue, a postman appeared, carrying his bag of letters as if nothing was out of the ordinary. 'Hitler ain't stopping me,' he said, raising his Royal Mail cap.

'Right bloody mess,' Ernie replied, shaking his head. 'I'm struggling to work out where I am.'

'St Luke's is my landmark.' The postman pointed in the direction of the old church. 'Couple of incendiaries put paid to the wood yard in Boyd Road yesterday, but they missed the church. This time, anyway.'

Turning to locate the spire through the dust clouds, Ernie nodded his thanks and headed towards it, just as he had done as a child when visiting Grandpa Henry. He smiled at the thought as he crossed the square. It was one of his happier memories. Spotting the towering horse chestnut tree in the churchyard, he remembered climbing it, shaking the branches and then fighting over the fallen conkers. It was in a sorry state – sap oozing from the burnt-off bark and not a leaf or prickly seed case in sight. In contrast, the church was packed. Scores of people who had lost their homes were huddled in every nook and cranny, their clothes torn and dirty, faces blackened by smoke, some caked with blood. For many of them, family members had been killed, injured or were missing.

A child's cry made him turn around. The little girl's red-raw feet were being treated for burns. 'She walked through red hot molasses, looking for me,' her mother said, seeing the look of concern on Ernie's face. 'Shoes are all burned. We're heading for Epping Forest as soon as me husband's found us a tent. Not staying here a minute longer. We watched people piling into Hallsville School on Saturday and it got a direct hit during the night.'

South Hallsville School, in Agate Street, was Ernie's school. Well, at least it would have been had he ever gone. Still, he felt a connection with it and what he was hearing made the hair stand up on the back of his neck.

'They were told buses were coming to take them away,' the woman continued. 'Waiting to be evacuated, but none came. Bloody disgusting!'

Her husband, who had just returned with an old pram containing tarpaulin and rope, filled in for her, spitting the words out in a mixture of anger and despair. 'Next message sent was, "Cancel the buses. Send us morgue vans and ambulances." The buses had gone to Camden Town, see, instead of Canning Town. It was a balls-up.' His voice faltered. 'We've lost half our relatives and friends, most of them kiddies.'

Ernie was stunned. All he could do was shake the man by the hand and watch as his wife made room in the pram for her bandaged daughter, cramming their few possessions in the rack below and making their way out of the church into the dust-filled daylight.

Spotting a woman bustling around offering cups of tea, Ernie crossed the aisle and gratefully accepted one with two sugars. He sat for a while surveying the people sorting themselves out as best they could, all of them knowing that nowhere was safe be it inside or out. He'd seen his fair share of destruction at the docks over the past few days, but the loss in human lives he was now contemplating was much harder to take. He knew he had to see Hallsville for himself.

There was a cordon around the school, or rather what was left of it. A parachute bomb had split the two-storey concrete building in two. Hundreds of tons of masonry had collapsed into the basement where people were sheltering in cramped conditions. Ernie pushed his way through a gap to see rescue workers clearing rubble from a twenty-foot crater. He could see straight away that no one could have survived, nor their bodies recovered.

He learned from one of the workers that around six hundred badly shaken-up people had been led there during the bombing on the Saturday night. The number was higher than it might have been due to the discovery of an unexploded device which landed on 8 Martindale Road, causing the whole street to be evacuated. They'd spent three nights crammed in the school basement, sitting in queues waiting for transport, before the direct hit at nearly four o'clock on the Tuesday morning.

Of course, no reports or pictures of the tragedy had appeared in the press; the effect on morale would be devastating. Someone said a man from West Ham Council had mentioned a figure of seventy-three victims, but those on the site knew it was far greater than that – more likely in the several hundred.

Ernie shot through the streets and alleys he knew like the back of his hand and was soon at 14 Bradley Street, Canning Town, which he was pleased to see looked unscathed. His Aunt Polly only had her youngest daughter living at home now. Her husband Jim had long since died and her eldest boy Alf, who had become too much for her to handle, was now in a home in Essex. All the family were relieved that that difficult decision had been made some time before war broke out, as he certainly wouldn't have coped with the bombing.

'Went down Rathbone Street first thing,' said Polly, eventually letting go of her nephew. For such a small woman, she had quite a grip. 'Stall keepers were doing their best to set up the market despite the mess and Lawrence Street, where you once lived, Ern, 'ad a few incendiaries through the roofs. But I couldn't believe my eyes when I saw Clarkson Street. It copped for an 'igh explosive on Sunday night.' Gasping and only halfway through her story, Polly refilled her cup from the teapot. 'I know Eliza Pridmore don't live there no more, but I couldn't 'elp thinking of 'er. There was this large crater where number 13 used to be and the 'ouses next door were teetering on the edge. They looked like they'd been sliced in 'alf with a knife and some of the upstairs rooms were jutting out in mid-air with their curtains blowing in the wind. Some of 'em still 'ad their wardrobes and beds! And as if Jerry 'adn't done enough damage, 'e dropped another load of incendiaries last night. Burnt out three 'ouses on the other side of the road.'

Relieved to hear that his aunt had agreed to move in temporarily with Daisy and Bill in Romford, Ernie bade his farewells and headed off for his last stop, which fortunately wasn't far from the King George V dock and the *Sirdar*.

Miraculously, a dusty bus weaved its way around the potholes and jutting tramlines on the Beckton Road, and it wasn't long before Ernie was in East Ham and turning down Manor Way. An overpowering stench made him cover his nose.

'Sewage works. Got hit on Sunday,' the conductor said matter-of-factly. 'Gas works come off worse, though. Real cocktail, ain't it?'

Straining his eyes to pick out the outline of the Gas, Light and Coke Company's works, Ernie could tell that the now largest gas works in Europe and adjoining tar works would take quite a while to make safe.

'The infants can't go to school due to an unexploded bomb in Winsor Terrace and a high explosive sent carrots and cabbages skyward in the Savage Garden allotments,' the conductor concluded, smiling.

As Ernie stepped off the bus at Cyprus, he could see smoke from the oil tanks still billowing skywards between the barrage balloons that were secured to lighters within the Albert Dock. Turning left at Beaconsfield Street, he was soon outside number 10. The two-up two-down had never looked any different from when he'd lived there nearly forty years ago. It was where he last saw his father and still sent shivers down his spine.

Cutting down Ferndale Street, the pub was still on the corner, and to his great relief he could see the whole row of shops and houses on Cyprus Place were still intact – even the old urinal opposite.

'Oh, Ern, I'm right pleased to see you,' the untidy confectioner and tobacconist of 17 Cyprus Place said, throwing her arms around her nephew. A few more pins fell out of her greying hair as she squeezed him tight just like her sister had.

'That goes for me too, Aunt Nance. I was getting worried about you, being so close to the Albert and all that.'

'Don't remind me. Every time a bomb drops in the dock, rats come pouring out and I swear they make a beeline for *my* shop. I've worn out me broom chasing 'em out.'

Ernie laughed; Nance had always been at war with rats.

'It's a good thing that Poll's getting out of Bradley Street,' she continued. 'Looks like I'm going to 'ave to carry on getting

215

in and out of the Andy shelter all the ruddy time. I'm that battered and bruised and you don't get a wink of sleep in one of them tin things. George is there now, tidying it up ready for tonight.'

'That's more to do with you insisting on dragging that blessed parrot in with you,' a familiar voice echoed from the back of the shop. 'Squawks louder than the bombs!'

George emerged from the gloom to shake hands with his cousin. 'You alright, Ern? 'Eard you 'ad your work cut out at the West India.'

Ernie shrugged. 'Didn't 'ave time to think about it – besides, everyone's doing their bit in the docks. Even the old-timers are working eleven-'our shifts right now. They salvaged sixty thousand tons of sugar from the North Quay warehouse.'

'You're not exactly a spring chicken yourself,' said George, shaking his head. 'That's where this war's different from the last. Just 'ave to pray it won't last long.'

''Ow's your shop doing… and 'arriet and the boys, of course?' asked Ernie, lightening the mood. Nance's son had taken over the grocers at 11 Cyprus Place when he married.

'Bacon slicer's gathering dust and can't say anyone's 'appy about only getting one egg a week, but we're all fine. Even young George now he's recovered from his exploits.'

'My grandson's an 'ero!' Nance said proudly, producing a local paper dated the beginning of June. 'Listen to this, Ern.'

Lad of fifteen was among Dunkirk Heroes
George William Pridmore, of 11 Cyprus Place, an apprentice on the Thames steam tug Sun IV, made two trips across the Channel, and his tug was responsible for saving hundreds of lives. George was fifteen only in March, and it is just a year since he left school. He would say little of his experiences, but his parents did gather that his tug had helped to rescue men from the hospital ship City of Paris, which was bombed by the Germans.

'When the tug left Ramsgate,' George continued, 'they'd 'ad

guns fitted on the bridge and were towing nine lifeboats. They got eighty-two Tommies in them on the first night, all wading through the water in single file with shells exploding all around. I'm so proud of 'im, Ern, 'e was gone five days and 'ad no sleep.'

How could boys aged only fifteen be involved in yet another war? Ernie asked himself as he neared the bascule bridge over the King George V dock. Barely a generation had passed since the end of the Great War which had taken so many young lives. Cousin John, fighting with the Canadians in France, came into his thoughts. Some had been luckier than others, and that's how it was going to be again.

* * *

Tugmaster Ernie with granddaughter Angela 1955

AUTHOR'S POSTSCRIPT

Ernie Pridmore retired from the PLA in 1956, having worked on the River Thames for forty-seven years, thirty-six of them as tugmaster. He and Ada remained in Brandon Street, Gravesend, and enjoyed over fifty years of marriage. Their parties were the talk of the town.

Ernie transferred from the *Sirdar* to the *Beam* in 1941. The *Sirdar* continued in the service of the PLA until 1950, when she was scrapped. After sinking in 1909, the *Britannia* was towed to Rotherhithe and, after extensive repairs, returned to service on the river until 1951. The SS *Indier*, towed to safety by the *Sirdar* during the first weekend of the Blitz, was torpedoed and sunk in the North Atlantic in April 1941. Only four of the forty-two on board survived.

Ernie never rekindled a relationship with his mother, but he always kept in touch with his siblings. Their childhood was lost at the hands of the West Ham Union, the youngest being released in 1915. By 1918, there were no children left in any Essex workhouse.Aunt Nance continued to run the shop in Cyprus Place until her death in 1951. Polly, too, remained in Bradley Street, reaching the grand old age of ninety-two. Confirmation that Joseph Pridmore did not die on Beckton Marshes only became clear during recent research. Whether Ernie knew the truth about his father will always remain a mystery.

The Bateman family continued to make a life for themselves in Canada, Amelia becoming a well-respected midwife in her local town. Her great-granddaughter, Kathy Mazzeo, has researched her family's East End origins and included John Pridmore in her family tree. One hundred and twenty thousand British Home children were sent to Canada until the scheme ended in 1939. Over ten per cent of the Canadian population is said to be a descendant of a British Home Child.

Will Thorne remained general secretary of the General and Municipal Workers Union until 1934. He served for many years on the West Ham Council and was Mayor from 1917–18. After contesting several elections as a Labour candidate, he finally won a seat representing West Ham South in the 1906 general election. In 1918, he won the seat of Plaistow with 94.9% of the vote and retained it until his retirement, aged eighty-seven, at the 1945 general election.

Daisy Parsons was elected Labour Councillor for Beckton ward in 1922. In 1931 she became Deputy Mayor of West Ham – the first woman to occupy the position and, in 1936, was elected Mayor. For her role in organising the women's voluntary service and the evacuation of local children during WW2, she was granted the freedom of West Ham in 1949. In 1951 she was awarded the MBE and in 2019 a blue plaque was erected outside Stratford Town Hall in her memory.

Eighty-five per cent of Canning Town's housing stock was destroyed in WW2, the heaviest damage in Tidal Basin ward, which contained some of the worst slums. Miraculously, St Luke's Church survived. East Ham Corporation built 934 prefabs (temporary homes) on Wanstead Flats and on open land around Cyprus which were designed to last ten years. Some were still there in 1985. Whilst the old houses and shops in Cyprus Place are long gone, the empty and boarded-up Ferndale pub is still there.

In 1953, my father – 'young Ernie' Pridmore – gave up working on the river to become a pub landlord. This was also the year I was born. If you know anything about running a pub you'll understand that it's pretty much a full-time job. I rarely saw my parents, which is why I spent most of my childhood with my grandparents – Ernie and Ada. If they ever questioned or resented having their retirement taken up looking after me, I never felt it. Quite the reverse: they cared for me, taught, played, indulged and, above all, loved me. As I did them.

The side gate of 42 Brandon Street, Gravesend, was left open for visitors. My Aunt Iris and my nan's sisters frequently popped in, as did Granddad's brother Joe, his sister Betsy and his cousins George and Daisy, who travelled down from East Ham. With Ada forever trying to stop her husband from playing practical jokes and tricks, especially on timid Betsy, the house was always filled with fun and laughter.

My grandfather spoke fondly of his aunts, particularly Nance and her shop in Cyprus Place. He told me that he had no shoes as a child, nor learned how to read or write. The story of how he and his brother, Bill, hid when their younger siblings were taken away to the workhouse filled me with fear. The fact that he became a Port of London tug skipper and that his actions on the first weekend of the Blitz gained him the George Medal have always made me proud and have become all the more significant since I began writing this book.

Angela Jean Young
Whitstable, 2021

Ernie

Bill

Joe

Betsy

Sarah

Nance

Polly

Daisy

ACKNOWLEDGEMENTS

Thanks go to my cousins Tony and Danny Wade for sharing their experiences as tuggies/Freemen of the Thames and for their memories of our grandparents. Also to Reggie Pridmore for details of his father's time in Shanghai. I owe a debt of gratitude to Kathy Mazzeo from Missouri, for the information she provided connecting the Bateman and Pridmore families. I am delighted that we discovered one another. My old friend Ann Debnam deserves a medal for her support and legwork over the years. Last but not least, special thanks go to Dick Thompson, who has always encouraged my writing and for sharing his knowledge of the Great War, which has proved invaluable.

USEFUL SOURCES

Newham Archive and Local Studies, Stratford Library, E15 1EL

Genealogy, Family Trees and Family History Records – www.ancestry.co.uk

Thames tugs 1833–2020 – www.thamestugs.co.uk

History of West Ham United – www.spartacus-educational.com

Britain's First Blitz 1914–1918 – www.iancastlezeppelin.co.uk

The Britannia disaster 1909 – research carried out by Brian Hayes, Gravesend

'Londoners over the Border – Canning Town', In *Household Words* by Charles Dickens, Henry Morley (1857)

The People of the Abyss by Jack London (first published in 1903)

West Ham – a study in social and industrial problems compiled by Edward G Howarth and Mona Wilson, JM Dent & Co (1907)

London Docks by John Pudney, Thames and Hudson (1975)

A Marsh and a Gasworks: one hundred years of life in West Ham by Newham History Workshop, Parents' Centre Publications (1986)

On the river – memories of a working river, An Age Exchange publication (1989)

Dockland Life 1860–1970 by Chris Ellmers and Alex Werner, Museum of London, Mainstream Publishing (1991)

The History of the Gas Light and Coke Company by Stirling Everard, A&C Black (Publishers) Limited (1992)

The Little Immigrants by Kenneth Bagnell, 1934, Dundurn Press (new edition 2001)

London 1900 by Jonathan Schneer, Yale University Press (2001)

Indoor Relief by Opal Gibson, Opal Publications (2006)

London Labour and the Poor 1849–50 by Henry Mayhew, Cosimo Classics (2013)

Chapters in the History of London Waterside Labour by H. Llewellyn Smith, Economic Journal, Oxford University Press (2014)

Gravesend in the Great War by Stephen Wynn, Pen and Sword Military (2016)

ABOUT THE AUTHOR

ANGELA JEAN YOUNG grew up in Gravesend, Kent. Her family has lived and worked on the River Thames for generations, which is what inspires her writing. Angela worked as a researcher in London's dynamic advertising scene before concentrating on writing and historical research. Today she lives and writes in Whitstable.